NATIONAL ANTHEMS OF THE WORLD

NATIONAL ANTHEMS
of the
WORLD

Edited by

MARTIN SHAW and HENRY COLEMAN

PITMAN PUBLISHING CORPORATION

LONDON - NEW YORK - TORONTO

First published in 1960
Second and revised edition 1963

© Copyright 1960 by Blandford Press Ltd.

PRINTED IN GREAT BRITAIN

CONTENTS

The anthems are arranged alphabetically except for
Bahrain and Qatar, which come at the end

Publisher's Preface and Acknowledgments

THE WORLD-WIDE RESPONSE to the first edition of this book, published in 1960, has given the opportunity now of including in this second edition a further 33 anthems: these are mainly the National Anthems of countries which have achieved independence since then, and there are some additional National Anthems or Songs not included in the first edition. There have also been one or two changes: Switzerland has made the Schweizerpsalm its official National Anthem for a trial period of three years; the United Arab Republic has a different anthem, and Syria now uses its own National Anthem.

A number of amendments have been made to anthems previously printed, and it has been possible to revise or enlarge the history notes on the composers, authors and origins in many cases.

In this revision work we are again indebted to the Embassies and their staffs who have supplied much of the information; to the Royal Marine School of Music, for their close liaison and consultation; and particularly to Dr. T. M. Cartledge, whose first-hand experience of many of these anthems at international conferences has been put liberally at our disposal.

The original idea for this book came from J. B. Cramer & Co. Ltd. who published a wartime collection of *National Anthems of the United Nations* edited by Martin Shaw. Upon the death of Dr. Shaw in 1959, the musical editorship of *National Anthems of the World* was taken over by Dr. Henry Coleman.

Acknowledgement is made at the foot of those anthems which are the copyright of J. B. Cramer & Co. Ltd. and other copyright material has been similarly acknowledged. Every effort has been made to trace copyright ownership, and it is regretted if any acknowledgments have been unwittingly omitted. In most cases the version in the melody and the accompaniment is that officially authorized by the State. Where piano arrangements and translations have been specially made, these may not be reproduced without the permission of Blandford Press Ltd.

Certain National Anthems have numerous verses, only one or two of which are customarily used, and so only these are given. Where English translations have been versified to fit the music, this has been done not so much for the purpose of singing (for the original language or languages would be used), but more to offer an indication of the meaning and so help in intelligent interpretation in singing the original words.

Where an anthem is in a language that is not written in Roman script, the words are given in a transliterated phonetic version to enable the anthem to be sung by those who cannot read it in its original form. This applies to the following:

Burma	Jordan	Sudan
Cambodia	Laos	Syria
China	Lebanon	Thailand
India	Libya	Tunisia
Israel	Muscat and Oman	United Arab Republic
Japan	Pakistan	Yemen

We acknowledge the work of Mr. Na'im Al-Basri who helped in the preparation of the musical arrangements of Libya, Jordan and Yemen and in the transliterated phonetic versions and translations of these and other Arabic countries.

We must also acknowledge the help of many officials and individuals all over the world who have given much information on important details. They are too numerous to list individually. Mention must, however, be made of Dr. Will Reed who has given advice and encouragement; and of Mr. Michael Karl Blackshaw, who put at our disposal material which he had assembled for a book on the same subject.

On various occasions we have consulted the Foreign Office, the Admiralty, the War Office, the BBC Music Library and the Royal Military School of Music, Kneller Hall, and acknowledge their assistance.

The main reference books consulted are Paul Nettl's *National Anthems* (1952, Storm Publishers, New York), Grove's *Dictionary of Music* (Macmillan), Collier's Encyclopedia (1959, New York), Murillo's *National Anthems of Countries of North, Central and South America* (1935).

Countries which are the dependent territories of other countries principally use the National Anthem of the " mother country." Where a country has in addition its own National Song which is used on important occasions, this is also given.

The final selection of anthems for such a volume as this must involve in some instances political and diplomatic implications, and the decision over this selection is that of the publisher.

It is hoped that this second edition of *National Anthems of the World* will continue to be a useful source book, not only for the increasing number of occasions on which it is desired to sing or play a particular anthem, but also as a reference book of considerable interest (as it has already proved) and as a record of the aspirations of the whole family of nations epitomised in the verses of these anthems.

AFGHANISTAN

No words

Music by
MOHAMMED FARUKH
Arr. by MOHAMMED MOKHTAR

Adopted as National Anthem, 1943

AFRICA
Nkosi Sikelel'i Africa

Words and Music by
ENOCH SONTONGA

Moderato con dignità

Nko - si si - ke - le - l'i Af - ri - ca, Ma - lu - pa - ka nyi - swu

du - mo lwa - yo;____ Yiz - wa i - mit - han - da zo ye - tu,

Nko - si si - ke - le - la,____ Nko - si si - ke - le - la.

B.2. si - ke - le, si - ke - le - la,

By permission of Lovedale Press, Cape Province, South Africa.
This is not an anthem for a nation but for a whole continent. Originating
with the Bantu people in South Africa, it is now sung throughout Africa in
various languages. The above version is in the Xosa language.
Anthems of individual African nations are included separately.

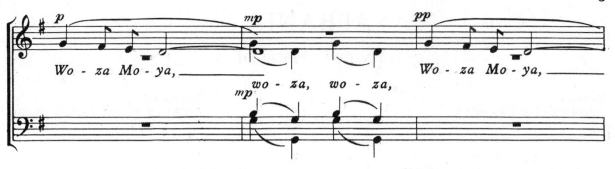

Wo - za Mo - ya, _____ Wo - za Mo - ya, _____
wo - za, wo - za,

wo - za, wo - za, Wo - za Mo - ya, O - yi - ngcwe - le,★

U - si si - ke - le - le, _____ Ti - na lu - sa - pho - lwa - yo.

Free Translation

God bless Africa,
Let her fame spread far and wide;
Hear our prayer,
May God bless us.
Come, Spirit, come,
Come, Holy Spirit,
Come and bless us, her children.

This song was composed in 1897 and first sung publicly in 1899. The composer died before it was published and his manuscript was eventually borrowed and lost. Some other musical arrangements have become known. Another version, published by Lovedale Press, is slightly different from the above; it is set in the key of B flat, has no repeat and terminates at the asterisk. The shorter version of the music is that used for the Tanganyika National Anthem.

ALBANIA

Hymni i Flamurit

Words by
ASDREN (A.S. DRENOVA)

Melody by
CIPRIAN PORUMBESCU (1880)
Arr. by HENRY COLEMAN

Adopted as National Anthem, 1912

cresc. molto

luf - te veç a - y lar - go - - het, Që ë -shtë lin - dur tra -dhë - -tor, Kush ë - shtë bu - rrë nuk fri -ko - het, Po vdes, po vdes si një dë - shmor. Prej - shmor.

Free Translation

The flag which in battle unites us
Found us all ready for the oath,
One mind, one aim, until our land
Becomes free from the enemy.
We stand in the battle for right and freedom,
The enemies of the people stand alone,
The hero dedicates his life to our land,
Even in dying he will be brave.

ANDORRA

Words by
The Hon. Dr. D. JOAN BENLLOCH I VIVÓ

Music by
Father ENRIC MARFANY

El gran Car-le-many, mon Pa - - re, dels a-larbs me des-lliu-rá,_____ i del cel vi-da em do-ná_____ de Me-rit-xell la gran Ma - re. Prin-

This became officially the National Anthem on the 8th September 1914,
the anniversary day of the Jungfrau von Meritxell, patron saint of Andorra.

-ce - sa nasquí i Pu - bi - lla en - tre dos na - cions neu -

-tral; _____ Sols res - to l'ú - ni - ca fi - lla del im-

-pe - ri Car - le - many. Cre - ient i lliu - re on - se

se - gles, cre - ient i lliu - re vull ser.

¡Si - guen els furs mos tu - tors i mos Prín - ceps de - fen - sors! i mos

Prín - ceps de - fen - sors! ___

Free Translation

The great Charlemagne, my Father, from the Saracens liberated me, and from heaven he gave me life of Meritxell the great Mother. I was born a Princess, a Maiden neutral between two nations; I am the only remaining daughter of the Carolingian empire. Believing and free eleven centuries, believing and free I will be. The laws of the land be my tutors and my defender Princes! and my defender Princes!

ARGENTINE

Words by
VICENTE LÓPEZ Y PLANES
(1784-1856)

Music by
BLAS PARERA (b. 1777)
Arr. by
JUAN PEDRO ESNAOLA (1808-1878)

Officially adopted as National Anthem, 11th May 1813, by the General Constituent Assembly of Argentina

B

rui - do de ro - tas ca - de - nas; Ved en

tro - na a la no - ble I-gual-dad.

¡Ya__ su tro - no dig-ní - si-mo a-brie - ron Las Pro-

-vin - cias U - ni - das del Sud! Y los

li - bres del mun - do res - pon - den: ¡Al gran

pue - blo Ar - gen - ti - no, Sa - lud!_____ ¡Al gran

pue - blo Ar - gen - ti - no, Sa - lud! Y____ los

li - bres del mun - do res - pon - den ¡Al gran

pue - blo Ar - gen - ti - no, Sa - lud!   Y___ los

li - bres del mun - do res - pon - den   ¡Al gran

pue - blo Ar - gen - ti - no, Sa - lud!

CHORUS
Allegro vivace

Sean e - ter - nos los lau - re - les. Que su - pi - mos con - se -

- guir: Que su - pi - mos con - se - guir: Co - ro -

Lento

- na - dos de glo - ria vi - va - - - mos O__ ju -

Allegro vivace

- re - mos con glo - ria mo - rir. O ju -

-re - mos con glo - ria mo - rir. O ju-

- re - mos con glo - ria mo - rir.

Free Translation

Hear, oh mortals! the sacred cry:
Freedom, freedom, freedom!
Hear the noise of broken chains;
See the throne of Equality the noble.

The United Provinces of the South
Their throne full of dignity opened!
And the free of the world reply:
A salutation to the great Argentine people!

CHORUS Let those laurels be eternal
Which we knew how to win:
Let us live crowned by glory
Or swear with glory to die.

AUSTRALIA

Advance Australia Fair

Words and Music by
PETER DODDS McCORMICK
("AMICUS") (1834-1916)
Arr. by H.A. CHAMBERS

1. Aus-tra-lia's sons, let us re-joice, For we are young and free; We've
2. When gal-lant Cook from Al-bion sail'd, To trace wide o-ceans o'er, True
3. While o-ther na-tions of the globe Be-hold us from a-far, We'll
4. Should for-eign foe e'er sight our coast Or dare a foot to land, We'll

gold-en soil and wealth for toil, Our home is girt by sea. Our
Brit-ish cour-age bore him on Till he land-ed on our shore. Then
rise to high re-nown and shine Like our glo-rious south-ern star. From
rouse to arms like sires of yore To guard our na-tive strand. Bri-

"God Save the Queen" is the National Anthem. No other anthem has
been officially adopted, yet many Australians regard "Advance Aus-
tralia Fair" in this light. This is played as a signature tune at most
Australian Radio Stations and T.V. Channels.

land a-bounds in Na-ture's gifts Of beau-ty rich and rare; In
here he raised old Eng-land's flag, The stan-dard of the brave; With
Eng-land, Sco-tia, E-rin's Isle, Who come our lot to share, Let
-tan-nia then shall sure-ly know, Be-yond wide o-cean's roll

his-t'ry's page let ev-'ry stage Ad-vance Aus-tra-lia fair.
all her faults we love her still—"Bri-tan-nia rules the wave."
all com-bine with heart and hand To ad-vance Aus-tra-lia fair.
sons in fair Aus-tra-lia's land Still keep a Brit-ish soul.

CHORUS (S.A.T.B.)

In joy-ful strains then let us sing, "Ad-vance Aus-tra-lia fair."

AUSTRIA
Österreichische Bundeshymne

Words by
PAULA PRERADOVIĆ (b.1887)

Music by
WOLFGANG AMADEUS MOZART (1756-1791)
Arr. by VIKTOR KELDORFER

Officially adopted as National Anthem by Austrian Cabinet 22nd October, 1946

Volk, be - gna - det für das Schö - ne, Viel - ge - rühm - tes
ho - her Sen - dung Last ge - tra - gen, Viel - ge - prüf - tes

Ö - ster - reich. Viel - ge - rühm - tes_ Ö - ster - reich.
Ö - ster - reich. Viel - ge - prüf - tes_ Ö - ster - reich.

3. *Mutig in die neuen Zeiten,*
   frei und gläubig sieh uns schreiten,
   arbeitsfroh und hoffnungsreich.
   Einig laß in Brüderchören,
   Vaterland, dir Treue schwören,
   Vielgeliebtes Österreich. (bis)

Free Translation

1. Land of mountains, land of streams, land of fields,
   land of spires, land of hammers, with a rich future,
   you are the home of great sons, a nation blessed by
   its sense of beauty,
   highly praised Austria, highly praised Austria.

2. Strongly fought for, fiercely contested, you are in
   the centre of the Continent like a strong heart, you
   have borne since the earliest days the burden of a
   high mission,
   much tried Austria, much tried Austria.

3. Watch us striding free and believing, with courage, into
   new eras, working cheerfully and full of hope, in
   fraternal chorus let us take in unity the oath of
   allegiance to you, our country,
   our much beloved Austria, our much beloved Austria.

BELGIUM
La Brabançonne

Words by
"JENNEVAL" (Hyppolite Dechet)
Last verse by
CHARLES ROGIER (1800-1885)
English translation by
MARY ELIZABETH SHAW and DICCON SHAW

Music by
FRANÇOIS VAN CAMPENHOUT (1779-1848)

1. O Va - der - land, o _ e - del land der Bel - gen, Zoo mach - tig
1. A - près des siè - cles _ d'es - cla - va - ge, _ Le _
1. From out the tomb of _ bon - dage and sla - ver - y _ Has

steeds _ door moed en werk - zaam - heid, _ De we - reld
Bel - ge, sor - tant du tom - beau, _
Bel - gium at last ris - en free; _

ziet ver - won - derd u we tel - gen Aan 't hoofd van
A re - con - quis par son cou - ra - ge Son _
And has re - cov - ered by her bra - ver - y, Her _

Written and composed in 1830 during the struggle between Belgium
and Holland for the independence of Belgium. Revised in 1951, when
the Flemish version replaced existing Flemish National Anthem.

kunst, van han - del, nij - ver - heid!
nom, ses droits___ et son dra - peau!
name, her flag, ___ her lib - er - ty;

De vrij - heids-
Et ta
And by your

-zon giet licht op u - we we - gen, En on - be-
main sou - ve - raine___ et ___ fië - re, Peu-
mien un - daunt - ed and vic - tor - ious Since that

-vreesd___ staart gij de toe - komst aan! Gij mint uw
-ple dé - sor - mais___ in - domp - té, Gra-
day, ___ up - hold - ing your cause, Is bla - zoned

vorst; zijn lief - de stroomt u te - - gen, Zijn hand ge-
-va sur ta vieil-le ban - niè - re Le
on your an - cient ban - ner glor - ious Your

-leidt _____ u op uw glo - rie - baan, Gij mint uw
Roi, _____ la loi, la li - ber - té! Gra -
King, _____ your free - dom and your laws. Is bla - zoned

vorst; zijn lief - de stroomt u te - - gen, Zijn hand ge-
-va sur ta vieil-le ban - niè - re Le
on your an - cient ban - ner glo - ious, Your

-leidt _____ u op uw glo - rie baan,
Roi, _____ *la loi, la li - ber - té!*
King, _____ your free-dom and your laws.

Zijn hand ge-
Le _____
Your _____

-leidt _____ u op uw glo - rie baan,
Roi, _____ *la loi, la li - ber - té!*
King, _____ your free-dom and your laws.

Zijn hand ge-
Le _____
Your _____

-leidt _____ u op uw glo - rie baan.
Roi, _____ *la loi, la li - ber - té!* _____
King, _____ your free-dom and your laws. _____

FLEMISH

2. Woei eens de storm ons toe uit vreemde streken,
   Blijft Vlaming, Waal, vereend met hart en ziel;
Ons voorgeslacht heeft nooit een stap geweken,
   Maar streed met moed en zegepraalde of viel!
Het roept ons toe: Bewaart 't erf uwer vaad'ren
   Bewaart uw roem; uw eendracht zij uw macht!
O luistert nooit naar lafaards en verraad'ren,
   Weg met al wie het Vaderland veracht.

3. Aan 't fiere land, waarvoor ons vaad'ren streden,
   Behoort ons hart, behoort ons goed en bloed!
Werd ooit de grens door vreemden overschreden,
   Wij schoten toe met Vlaamschen heldenmoed!
Laat overal 't driekleurig vaandel wapp'ren
   In dorp en stad, bij burger en sol daat.
Dat zinnebeeld is heilig voor de dapp'ren:
   Wee hem die 't ooit wou schennen of versmaadt.

FRENCH

2. Marche de ton pas énergique,
   Marche de progrès en progrès;
Dieu, qui protège la Belgique,
   Sourit à tes mâles succès.
Travaillons: notre labeur donne
   A nos champs la fécondité,
Et la splendeur des arts couronne
   Le Roi, la loi, la liberté.

3. O Belgique, ô mère chérie,
   A toi nos cœurs, à toi nos bras,
A toi notre sang, ô Patrie,
   Nous le jurons tous, tu vivras!
Tu vivras toujours grande et belle,
   Et ton invincible unité
Aura pour devise immortelle:
   Le Roi, la loi, la liberté.

ENGLISH

2. March on! with steady unfailing paces
   From progress to progress march on.
Still, through misfortune, on your faces
   God's smile, protecting you, has shone.
Let us work! for labour, life-bestowing,
   From the earth her fertile produce draws,
And crowns, with splendour ever brightly glowing,
   Your King, your freedom and your laws.

3. Beloved Belgium, beloved Mother,
   Our arms, our hearts, our blood we give
Freely to you, and to none other;
   And by these we swear that you shall live.
Shall live in beauty and in strength for ever
   Holding fast, as watchword of your cause,
The deathless bond that binds your sons together
   Your King, your freedom and your laws.

BOLIVIA

Words by
JOSE IGNACIO de SANJINÉS
(1786-1864)
Translated by
G. H. HATCHMAN
Versified by
SEBASTIAN SHAW

Music by
BENEDETTO VINCENTI

1.Bo - li - via - nos: el ha - do pro - pi - cio co - ro - no___ nues-tros vo - tos y an-he - lo; es ya

1.Oh Bo - li - via, our long felt de - sires,___ By the kind - li-ness of des - ti-ny are crowned now. Here, where

Played for first time in 1842 and adopted the same year.
José de Sanjinés was a jurist and signer of the Bolivian Declaration of Independence.
By permission J.B. Cramer & Co. Ltd.

li - bre ya li - bre es - te sue - - - lo, ya__ ce -
free - dom, our free - dom, is found now, E - ver from

-só su ser-vil__ con - di - ción. Al es -
bon - dage we cel - e - brate re - lease. Af - ter

-truen - do marcial que a yer fue - - ra y al cla -
all the mar - tial clam - our that as - pires__ To the

-mor__ de la gue - rra ho - rro - ro - - so, si - guen
clash of war - fare's hi - de-ous in - sa - ni - ty, Now in

hoy___ en con-tras - te ar - mo - nio - - so dul-ces
con - trast hear the mu - sic of hu - ma - ni - ty, Joy - ful

him - nos de paz___ y___ de u - nión.
hymns of sweet u - ni - ty___ and peace.
Si - guen
Now in

cresc.

hoy___ en con-tras - te ar - mo - nio - - so___ dul - ces
con - trast hear the mu - sic of hu - ma - ni - ty,___ Joy - ful

cresc.

him - nos de paz___ y___ de u - nión.
hymns of sweet u - ni - ty___ and peace.
De la
E - ver-

ff

f CHORUS

ff

f

an - tes que es-cla - vos vi-vir!
death than ex-is - tence as slaves!

2. *Esta tierra inocente y hermosa*
   que ha debido a Bolívar su nombre,
   es la Patria feliz donde el hombre
   goza el bien de la dicha y la paz.
   Que los hijos del grande Bolívar
   han ya mil y mil veces jurado
   morir antes que ver humillado
   de la Patria el augusto pendón.

   CORO: De la Patria etc.

3. *Loor eterno a los bravos guerreros*
   cuyo heróico valor y firmeza
   conquistaron las glorias que empieza
   hoy Bolivia feliz a gozar.
   Que sus nombres el mármol y el bronce
   a remotas edades trasmitan
   y en sonoros cantares repitan
   ¡Libertad, Libertad, Libertad!

   CORO: De la Patria etc.

2. Here where Justice has raised up her throne,
   Long denied her by the evil of oppression,
   Her flung banners find glorious expression
   We are free, we are free, we are free!
   Sons, whom mighty Bolivar shall call his own,
   Have a thousand thousand times in great solemnity
   Freely offered life itself as sworn indemnity,
   If dishonoured their flag should ever be.

   CHORUS: Evermore, Motherland etc.

3. Those brave warriors eternally praise,
   Whose courage, unexampled, evermore is
   The foundation of all the proud glories
   To which happy Bolivia is heir.
   Lettered bronze and marble gratefully we'll raise
   That their deeds may live for distant generations,
   And our sons' and grandsons' joyful salutations
   Shall, in song, honour still the great names there.

   CHORUS: Evermore, Motherland etc.

BRAZIL

Words by
JOAQUIM OSÓRIO DUQUE ESTRADA
(1870–1927)
Translated by
GASTÃO NOTHMAN
Versified by
SEBASTIAN SHAW

Music by
FRANCESCO MANOEL da SILVA
(1795–1865)

The music was written for the National Anthem in 1831. In 1922
a new text was officially adopted and the same tune retained.

By permission of J. B. Cramer & Co. Ltd.

VERSE

1. Ou - vi - ram do Y - pi - ran - ga as mar - gens
1. From peace - ful Y - pi - ran - ga's banks rang

plá - ci - das De um po - vo he-roi - co o bra - do re - tum -
out a cry, A chal - lenge from a peo - ple who were

- ban - te, E o sol da li - ber - da - de em rá - ios
fear - less; Thence - forth the sun of Free - dom climbed our

fúl - gi - dos, Bri - lhou no céu da Pá - tria nes - se in
coun - try's sky, And poured its rays up - on us, bright and

stan - te, Se o pe - nhor___ des-sa i - gual - da - de Con - se-
peer - less. We, with breasts bared, de - fy, oh Free - dom, Death it -

- gui - mos con - quis - tar com bra - ço for - te, Em teu
- self, for the e - qua - li - ty you taught us! Striv - ing

sei - o, Oh, Li - ber - da - de, De - sa -
fierce - ly, here in your bo - som, To be

- fi - a o nos - so pei - to a pró - pria mor - te! Oh! Pá - tria a -
worth - y of this prec - ious gift you brought us. O glor - ious

-ma - da, i - do - la - tra - da, Sal - ve! Sal - ve! Bra-
and be - lov - ed land, hail! Hail Bra - zil!_____ Be-

-sil, um so - nho in - ten - so um rá - io ví - vi - do De a-
-hold a won - drous vi - sion, lo! a dazz - ling ray Of

-mor e de es - pe - ran - ça à ter - ra des - ce, Se em
love and hope, from heav'n to earth, trans - cen - dent! Our

teu for - mo - so céu, ri - so - nho e lím - pi - do, A i-
smil - ing skies, in lim - pid beau - ty, now dis - play A

- ra - da, en - tre ou - tras mil, és tu, Bra - sil, Oh! Pá - tria a -
thou - sand, You ev - er will Be, oh Bra - zil, The one dear

- ma - da! dos fi - lhos dês - te so - lo és mãe gen -
home - land! Oh bount - eous mo - ther, with such love you

- til, Pá - tria a - ma - da, Bra - sil!
fill Your proud chil - dren, Bra - zil!

- sil !
- zil !

2. *Deitado eternamente em berço esplendido,*
    Ao som do mar e à luz do ceu profundo,
    Fulguras, Brasil, florão da América,
    Iluminado ao sol do novo mundo.
    Do que a terra mais garrida
    Teus risonhos, lindos campos têm mais flores,
    Nossos bosques têm mais vida,
    Nossa vida no teu seio mais amores.
        Oh! Pátria amada, idolatrada,
        Salve! Salve!
    Brasil, de amor eterno seja o símbolo
    O lábaro que ostentas estrelado,
    E diga o verde louro dessa flámula
    Paz no futuro e glória no passado.
    Mas, se ergues da justiça a clava forte
    Verás que um filho teu não foge à luta
    Nem teme quem te adora a própria morte.
        Terra adorada entre, outras mil, és tu, Brasil,
        Oh! Pátria amada! dos filhos dêste solo és mãe gentil,
        Pátria amada, Brasil!

2. To ocean's music, under skies of deepest blue,
    America's fair flower, fading never,
    In splendour you lie cradled. Oh Brazil, on you
    The sun of this New World shines down for ever!
    Oh, far more than in fair lands elsewhere,
    Your sweet pastures are bedecked with smiling blossom;
    Your vast woodlands a greater life share,
    And a deeper love we know within your bosom.
        Oh glorious and beloved land, hail! Hail Brazil!
    Then let your starry ensign never cease to fly,
    Symbolic of the love that fills your story;
    And let the verdant laurels on your pennon cry :-
    "In future peace and in the past great glory!"
    But if, in justice, you should raise your mighty sword,
    You shall not see a son of yours from battle flee,
    Nor shall he fear to die for you, whom he adored.
        Amongst a thousand,
        You ever will
        Be, oh Brazil,
        The one dear homeland!
        Oh bounteous mother, with such love you fill
        Your proud children, Brazil!

BRUNEI

Words by
PENGIRAN MAHOMED YUSEF bin
PENGIRAN HAJI ABDUL RAHIM

Music by
INCHE AWANG BESAR bin SAGAP
Arr. by HENRY COLEMAN

This anthem was composed in 1947 through the initiative of a group of youths who decided that their country should have a National Anthem, and chose two of their number to write and compose it. It was officially adopted in 1951.

Me - mim - pin ra'a - yat ke - kal baha - gi - a;

Hi - dup sen - to - sa Ne - ga - ra dan Sultan,

I - la - hi se - la - mat - kan Bru - nei Da - rus sa - lam.

Free Translation

Oh God, Long Live our Majesty the Sultan;
Justice and Sovereignty in sheltering our
country and leading our people;
Prosperity to our Nation and Sultan.
God Save Brunei.

BULGARIA
Shoumi Maritsa

Music by
GABRIEL SEBEK
Arr. by HENRY COLEMAN

1. Shou - mi Ma - ri - tsa o - kar - va - ve - na,

Pla - che vdo - vi - tsa, lyu - to ra - ne - na.

Marsh,_____ marsh,_____ s'ge - ne - ra - la na - sh,

This National Anthem dates from the year 1885, but is not at present sung inside
Bulgaria as the anthem which follows has officially replaced it.

V'boy da le - tim i vrag da po - be - dim! -dim!

2. *Balgarsky cheda, tsyal svyat vi gleda,*
   V' boy za pobeda, slavno da varvim.
   Marsh, marsh s'Generala nash,
   v'boy da letim i vrag da pobedim!

3. *Lavat Balkansky, v'boy velikansky,*
   s'ordi doushmansky, vodi ni krilat.
   Marsh, marsh s'Generala nash,
   v'boy da letim i vrag da pobedim!

English Translation

1. Maritsa rushes, stained with blood,
   A widow wails, fiercely wounded.
   March, march, with our General,
   Let's fly into battle and crush the enemy!

2. Bulgarians, the whole world beholds you.
   Into a winning battle, let's gloriously go.
   March, march, with our General,
   Let's fly into battle and crush the enemy!

3. The Balkan lion leads us flying
   Into a gigantic battle with the enemy hordes.
   March, march, with our General,
   Let's fly into battle and crush the enemy!

BULGARIA

Bulgaria mila, zemya na gheroi

Words by
NIKOLA FURNADZIEV, M. ISACVAND and
ELIZAVETA BAGRIANA

Translated by
KATYA BOYADJIEVA

Music by
GEORGI DIMITROV
GEORGI ZLATEV-TSCHERKIN and
SVETOSLAV OBRETENOV

This officially replaced 'Shoumi Maritza' as the National Anthem in 1946
A competition for a new National Anthem was announced in September, 1962

CHORUS

Hail, our Republic, we sing to your glory!
May you fore'er be a true shield of peace!–
But should an enemy storm o'er the country,
Lead us to battle, to glorious feats!

1. Bulgaria, dear, you're the land of our heroes!
Incessant and mighty has surged your ascent.
The link with our brothers shall grow ever stronger;
The firm, soldier's link with the Soviet land!

2. How great is the sun of our Lenin and Stalin,
Whose unequalled splendour throws light on our way!
The hearts which Dimitrov has fired are flaming
In struggle and work with so dazzling a ray!

3. We're digging our mines, we are working and building,
We're tilling in common the large tract of soil.
Our country, our beautiful country thus serving
With all that we have, with our lives and our toil.

BURMA

Words by
GROUP OF BURMESE
English versification by
T.M.CARTLEDGE

Music by
TH KIN BA THOUNG
Arr. by T. M. CARTLEDGE

Adagio

This officially became the National Anthem in 1948.

Da do byay da do myay do baing way myay.
This is our coun - try, our land, ours by right.

Do' byay do myay adjo - go
We for her the task re -

nyi - nya zwa do dudway. Tang saung ba tso lay
- spon - sib - ly shoul - der. As one we stand in

do da - won bay apo dan myay.★
du - ty to our pre - cious land.

★At the end of the anthem it is customary for the singers to give a slight bow.

CAMBODIA
Nokoreach

Words by
CHUON-NAT

Adapted from a Cambodian folk song
by F. PERRUCHOT and J. JEKYLL
Arr. by HENRY COLEMAN

1. Som pouk tep - da rak sa moha Khsath yeung_____ Oy ban roung roeung doy chey mon - kol___ srey sour - sdey Yeung Khnhom preah ang som chrok Krom moloup preah Ba - ro -

Adopted as the Royal and National Anthem, 1941, reaffirmed 1947

- mey _____ Ney preah No-rop-dey vong Khsat-tra del sang preah sat

thmâr Kroup Kraung dèn Kkmer bo-rann thkoeung thkann.2. **Pra**-sath sé-
3.*Kroup vath a- kor.*

2. *Prasath séla kombang kan dal prey*
Kuor oy srâmay noeuk dâl yuos sak Moha Nokor
Cheat Khmer dauch Thmar kong vong nôy lâar rung peung chom hor.
Yeung sang Khim por pheap preng samnang robuos Kampuchea.
Moha râth koeut mien you ang veanh hey.

3. *Kroup vath aram lû tè so sap thoeur*
Sot doy am nô rom lik koun poth sasna
Chol yeung chea neak thioeur thiak smos smak tam bêp donnta
Kong tè thévoda nùng chuoy chrom chrèng phkôt phkang pra yoch oy
Dol prateah Khmer chea Moha Nokor.

French Translation

1. *Que le ciel protège notre Roi*
   Et lui dispense le bonheur et la gloire.
   Qu'il règne sur nos cœurs et sur nos destinées
   Celui qui, héritier des Souverains bâtisseurs,
   Gouverne le fier et vieux Royaume.

2. *Les temples dorment dans la forêt*
   Rappelant la grandeur du Moha Nokor
   Comme le roc, la race khmère est éternelle
   Ayons confiance dans le sort du Campuchéa
   L'Empire qui défie les années.

3. *Les chants montent dans les pagodes*
   A la gloire de la Sainte foi Bouddhique.
   Soyons fidèles aux croyances de nos pères.
   Ainsi le ciel prodiguera-t-il tous ses bienfaits
   Au vieux pays khmer, le Moha Nokor.

English Translation

1. Heaven protects our King
   And gives Him happiness and glory
   To reign over our souls and our destinies
   The one being, heir of the Sovereign **constructors**
   Guiding the proud old Kingdom.

2. Temples are asleep in the forest
   Remembering the splendour of Moha Nokor.
   Like a rock the Khmer race is eternal.
   Let us trust in the fate of Campuchea
   The empire which challenges the ages.

3. Songs rise up from the pagodas,
   To the glory of holy buddhistic faith.
   Let us be faithful to our ancestors' belief.
   Thus heaven will lavish its bounty
   Towards the ancient Khmer country, the Moha Nokor.

CAMEROON

Chant de Ralliement

Words by RENE JAM AFAME
and a group of students
English versification by
T. M. CARTLEDGE

Music by
SAMUEL MINKYO BAMBA
and MOISE.NYATE
Arr. by HENRY COLEMAN

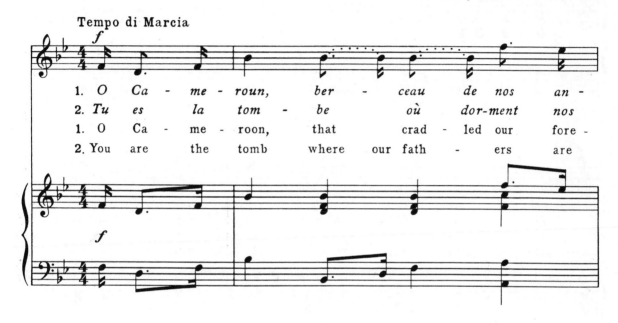

This anthem was written and composed in 1928 by students from l'Ecole Normale de la
Mission Presbytérienne Américaine de Foulassi à Sangmelina, Cameroun. It was adopted as
the unofficial National Anthem in 1948 and became the official Anthem on 10th May, 1957

- rie.___ Comme un so - leil tu commences à pa -
- vé.___ Nous tra - vail - lons pour te ren - dre pros -
days.___ But like the ris - ing___ sun now ap -
- ceived.___ We work that you may be - come fair and

- raî - tre; Peu à peu tu sors de ta sau - va - ge -
- pè - re, Un beau jour en - fin nous se - rons ar - ri -
- pear - ing, Bit by bit you now are leav - ing sav - age
pros - p'rous, And one day at last we'll see it all a -

- ri - e. Que___ tous tes en-fants du___ Nord au Sud, De___
- vés.___ De l'A - fri-que soit fi-dèle___ en - fant Et___
ways.___ May___ all your child-ren fol-low the com-mand, From___
- chieved.___ May you be a faith-ful child of Af - ri - ca, Advancing

Ped. *

l'Est à l'Ouest soient tout a - mour.____ Te ser - vir que ce soit__ leur__ seul_
pro-gres-se tou - jours en Paix,____ Es-pé-rant que__ tes__ jeunes en -
East and West to give their heart,____ Their on - ly wish_ to__ serve their
stead-i - ly__ in__ peace,____ In hope that ev - 'ry young child_ of

but Et____ rem - plir leur de - voir tou-jours.
-fants T'ai - me - ront sans bornes à ja - mais.
land And with con - stan - cy all play their part.
yours Will__ love you un - til time__ shall__ cease.

CHORUS
ff

Chère Pa - tri - - e, terre ché - ri - - e, Tu
This our land that we all love so, On

ff

CANADA
O Canada

Words (in French) by
SIR ADOLPHE BASILE ROUTHIER, (1839-1920)
Translated by
R. STANLEY WEIR
(1856-1926)

Music by
CALIXA LAVALEE
(1842-1891)
Arr. by H.A. CHAMBERS

1. O Can - a - da! Our home and na - tive land!
2. O Can - a - da! Where pines and ma - ples grow,
3. O Can - a - da! Be - neath thy shin - ing skies
4. Ru - ler su - preme, Who hear - est hum - ble pray'r,

home and na - tive land! True pa - triot - love in
pines and ma - ples grow, Great prair - ies spread and
neath thy shin - ing skies May stal - wart sons and
hear - est hum - ble pray'r, Hold our Do - min - ion

CHORUS (S.A.T.B. *ad lib.*)

O Can - a - da!
O ____ Can - a - da! ____ Glo - rious and free!

We stand on guard, We stand on guard for thee,

O Can - a - da! We stand on guard for ____ thee.

FRENCH

1. O Canada! Terre de nos aïeux,
   Ton front est ceint de fleurons glorieux!
   Carton bras sait porter l'épée,
      Il sait porter la croix!
   Ton histoire est une épopée
      Des plus brillants exploits.
   Et ta valeur, de foi trempée,
   Protégera nos foyers et nos droits. (bis)

2. Sous l'œil de Dieu, près du fleuve géant.
   Le Canadien grandit en espérant.
   Il est né d'une race fière,
      Béni fut son berceau.
   Le ciel a marqué sa carrière
      Dans ce monde nouveax.
   Toujours guidé par sa lumière,
   Il gardera l'honneur de son drapeau. (bis)

3. De son patron, précurseur du vrai Dieu,
   Il porte au front l'auréole de feu.
   Ennemi de la tyrannie
      Mais plein de loyauté.
   Il veut garder dans l'harmonie,
      Sa fière liberté;
   Et par l'effort de son génie,
   Sur notre sol asseoir la vérité. (bis)

4. Amour sacré du trône et de l'autel.
   Remplis nos cœurs de ton souffle immortel!
   Parmi les races étrangères,
      Notre guide est la loi:
   Sachons être un peuple de frères,
      Sous le joug de la foi.
   Et répétons, comme nos pères,
   Le cri vainqueur: "Pour le Christ et le roi". (bis)

CANADA
The Maple Leaf for Ever

Words and Music by
ALEXANDER MUIR (1830-1906)
Arr. by H. A. CHAMBERS

1. In days of yore, from Brit-ain's shore, Wolfe, the daunt-less he-ro came, And plant-ed firm Brit-an-nia's flag On Canada's fair domain. Here may it wave, our
2. At Queens-ton heights and Lun-dy's lane, Our brave fa-thers, side by side, For free-dom, homes, and loved ones dear, Firm-ly stood and no-bly died; And those dear rights which
3. Our fair Do-min-ion now ex-tends From Cape Race to Noot-ka Sound; May peace for ev-er be our lot, And plen-teous store a-bound: And may those ties of

This National Song is also used on some occasions. It was written and composed in 1867.

boast, our pride, And, joined in love to - ge - ther, The
they main - tained, We swear to yield them nev - er! Our
love be ours, Which dis - cord can - not sev - er, And

This - tle, Sham - rock, Rose en - twine The Ma - ple Leaf for ev - er!
watch - word ev - er - more shall be, The Ma - ple Leaf for ev - er!
flour - ish green o'er Free - dom's home, The Ma - ple Leaf for ev - er!

CHORUS

The Ma - ple Leaf, our em - blem dear, The Ma - ple Leaf for ev - er! God

save our Queen and Hea - ven bless The Ma - ple Leaf for ev - er!

4. On mer - ry Eng-land's far - famed land   May kind Hea - ven sweet - ly smile; God

MELODY

4. On mer - ry Eng - land's far-famed land   May kind Hea - ven sweet - ly smile;   God

bless old Scot - land ev - er-more, And   Ire-land's Em - 'rald Isle!

bless old Scot - land   ev - er - more, And_ Ire-land's Em - 'rald Isle!   Then

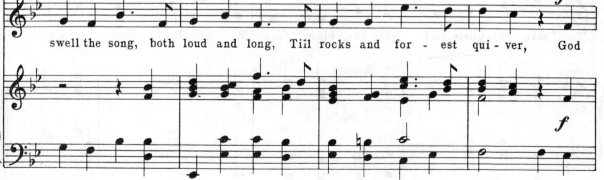

Then swell the song, Till rocks and for - est qui - ver,   God

swell the song, both loud and long, Till rocks and for - est qui - ver,   God

CENTRAL AFRICAN REPUBLIC
La Renaissance

Words by BARTHÉLEMY BOGANDA

Music by HERBERT PEPPER

This National Anthem was adopted by the National Assembly on 25th May 1960.
The words are by the first President of the Central African Republic.

Dans le tra - vail, l'ordre et la di - gni - té,

Tu re - con - quiers ton droit, ton u - ni - té,

Et pour fran - chir cette é - ta - pe nou - vel - le,

De nos an - cê - tres la voix____ nous ap - pel - le.

Ped.   Ped.

Ped.   Ped.

CHORUS

Au tra-vail dans l'ordre et la di-gni-té, Dans le res-pect du

(Xylophones)

droit dans l'u-ni-té, Bri-sant la mi-sè-re et la ty-ran-nie,

Brandissant l'é-ten-dard _____ de la Pa-trie. _____

ff

Ped.

Translation by
T.M. CARTLEDGE

Oh! Central Africa, cradle of the Bantu people!
Take up again your right to respect, to life!
Long subjugated, long scorned by all,
But, from today, breaking tyranny's hold.
Through work, order and dignity
You reconquer your rights, your unity,
And to take this new step
The voice of our ancestors calls us.

Chorus

To work! In order and dignity,
In the respect for rights and in unity,
Breaking poverty and tyranny,
Holding high the flag of the Fatherland.

CEYLON
Namō Namō Mathā

Words and melody by
ANANDA SAMARAKOON
Arr. by **SURYA SENA**

Adopted as National Anthem, 1952

2. *Obave apa vidya obamaya apa sathya*
   ..... obave apa shakti
   apa hada thula bhakti oba apa āloke
   apage anuprane oba apa jeevana ve
   apa muktiya obave

3. *Nava jēēvana demine nithina apa*
   pubudu karan māthā
   Gnana vēērya vadavamina ragena yanu
   mana jaya bhōōmi karā
   Eka mavekuge daru kala bavinā
   yamu yamu wee nopamā
   Prema vadamu sama bheda durara
       Namō Namō Māthā

Free Translation by Dr. C. W. W. Kannangara

Mother Lanka— we worship Thee!
Plenteous in prosperity, Thou,
Beauteous in grace and love,
Laden with corn and luscious fruit
And fragrant flowers of radiant hue,
Giver of life and all good things,
Our land of joy and victory,
Receive our grateful praise sublime,
Lanka! we worship Thee.

Thou gavest us Knowledge and Truth,
Thou art our strength and inward faith,
Our light divine and sentient being,
Breath of life and liberation.
Grant us, bondage free, inspiration.
Inspire us for ever.
In wisdom and strength renewed,
Ill-will, hatred, strife all ended,
In love enfolded, a mighty nation
Marching onward, all as one,
Lead us, Mother, to fullest freedom.

CHAD
La Tchadienne

Words by
Father GIDROL, S.J. and
students of St. Paul's School★

Music by
Father VILLARD, A.J.,
Arr. by Col. P. DUPONT

★St. Paul's School at Fort Archambault trains
teachers for Catholic education in Chad.

Fine

-tra de ton cou-ra - ge. Lè - ve les yeux, l'a-ve-nir est à Toi.

mf **Verse**

O mon Pa - ys, _____

_____ que Dieu te prenne en gar - de,

Que tes voi - sins ad - mi- rent tes en-fants. Jo-

yeux, pa - ci - fique, a - vance en - chan - tant, Fi - dèle à tes an -

ciens qui te re - gar - - - dent.

English Translation
by T.M.Cartledge

CHORUS

People of Chad, arise and take up the task!
You have conquered the soil and your rights;
Your freedom will be born of your courage.
Lift up your eyes, the future is yours.

VERSE

Oh, my Country, may God protect you,
May your neighbours admire your children.
Joyful, peaceful, advance as you sing,
Faithful to your fathers who are watching you.

Repeat Chorus

CHILE

Words by
EUSEBIO LILLO (1826-1910)

Music by
RAMÓN CARNICER
(1789-1855)

The original words of this National Anthem were written in 1819.   In 1847 when a new Peace
Treaty was signed between Chile and Spain, the Chilean government requested Eusebio Lillo
to write new words, without bitterness towards Spain, the 'mother country'.

Chi - le es tu cie - lo_a - zu - la - - - do pu - - ras
Chi - le, thy skies__ spread a - bove__ thee, So__

bri - sas__ te cru - zan__ tam - bién, y tu
sweet__ are__ the breez - es__ that roam O'er thy

cam - po de flo - res bor - da - - - do es la
fields__ rich - ly broi - dered with flow - er - lets That__

co - pia fe - liz__ del E - dén. Ma - ges -
an - gels might make__ thee their home! Grand - ly

-tuo - sa es la blan - ca mon - ta - - ña que te
ri - ses the snow - cov - ered moun - - tain The___

dió por ba - luar - te el Se - ñor, que te
ram - part be - stowed by the Lord, The___

dió por ba - luar - te el_ Se - ñor, y e - se
ram - part be stowed___ by___ the Lord, And the

mar___ que tran - qui - lo__ te ba - ña te pro -
sea___ like a tran - quil___ foun - tain Of thy

-me - te fu-tu - ro es - plen - dor._____ y___ e - se
fu - ture___ whis - pers its word.___ And___ the___

mar___ que tranqui - lo te ba - ña te___ pro -
sea___ like a tran - quil___ foun - tain Of___ thy___

-me - te fu-tu - ro es - plen - dor.
fu - ture___ whis - pers its word.

CHORUS

Dul - - - ce Pa - - tria, re -
Dear_____ Home - - - land ac -

-ci - - be los vo - tos
-cept the vows

con que Chi - - le en tus
On thine al - - tars that

a - - ras ju - ró que o la
Chi - le shall be A

tum - ba se - rá de los li - bres o el a -
re - fuge from for - eign op - pres - sion Or the

-si - lo con-tra la o - pre - sión   que o la
glo - rious__ home   of   the   free!   A ___

tum - ba se - rá__ de los li - - bres o el a -
re - fuge from for - eign op - pres - - sion   Or the

-si - lo con-tra__ la o - pre - sión   que o la tum - ba se -
glo - rious__ home__ of the free,   A ___ re - fuge from

rá   de los li - bres o el a -
for - - eign op - pres - sion   Or the

CHINA
(Nationalist)

Words based on a speech by
Dr. SUN YAT-SEN (1867-1925)
Translated by
TU T'ING-HSIU

Music by
CHE'NG MAO-YÜN (1928)
Arr. by
Professor HUANG CHIH

San min chu I, wo tang so
"San min chu I," our aim shall

chung, I kien min kuo, I chin - ta
be, To found a free land, world peace be our

tung. Tze erh to shih, wei min chien feng, su
stand. Lead on com-rades, van-guards ye are, Hold

Adopted as the National Anthem in 1929
The words 'San Min Chu I' express Dr. Sun's political philosophy
of the Three People's Principles, i.e. government of the people, by
the people, and for the people.

yeh fei shieh, chu I shih tsung, shih ching shih ___
fast your aim, by sun and star, Be earn - est and

yung, pi shing pi ___ chung, I
brave, your coun - try to save, One

hsin I ___ teh, kuan cheh shih ___ chung!
heart, one ___ soul, one mind one ___ goal!

CHINA
Communist

Words by T'IEN HAN

Music by NIE ERH

This song was written in 1932. On the 27th September 1949 it
was officially approved as the National Anthem of Communist China.
Reproduced from Die National-Hymnen der Erde by permission of
the publisher, Max Hueber Verlag.

Unofficial Translation

Rise! We do not want to be slaves,
Build anew the long wall from flesh and blood,
For China's people is in greatest danger
And the oppressed cry loud from fury.
Oh rise, oh rise, oh rise,
Millions we are, and yet but one in heart,
For we throw ourselves with courage on the enemy,
Forward,
For we throw ourselves with courage on the enemy,
Forward, forward, forward!

COLOMBIA

Words by
RAFAEL NUÑEZ
(1825-1894)

Music by
ORESTES SÍNDICI

This anthem was sung for the first time c. 1905. Rafael Nuñez was elected
President of Colombia four times.

VERSE

1. Ce - só la ho-rri - ble___ no - che, La li - ber-tad___ su-

- bli - me De - rra-ma las___ au - ro - ras

De su in-ven-ci - ble luz. La hu - ma - ni-dad en -

- te - ra, Que en - tre ca-de - nas gi - me, Com -

-pren - de las pa-la - bras Del que murió en la Cruz.

2. *INDEPENDENCIA grita*
    El mundo americano;
    Se baña en sangre de héroes
    La tierra de Colón.
    Pero este gran principio:
    EL REY NO ES SOBERANO,
    Resuena, y los que sufren
    Bendicen su pasión.

CHORUS

Oh unfading glory!
Oh immortal joy!
In furrows of pain
Good is already germinating.

1. The fearful night came to an end,
    Liberty sublime
    Is spreading the dawns
    Of its invincible light.
    The whole of humanity,
    Which is groaning under chains,
    Understands the words
    Of the One who died on the Cross.

2. INDEPENDENCE cries
    The American world;
    In heroes' blood is bathing
    The Land of Columbus.
    But this great principle:
    THE KING IS NOT SOVEREIGN,
    Resounds, and those who suffer
    Praise the passion in it.

CONGO (Brazzaville)★
La Congolaise

Words and Melody by
JEAN ROYER
JACQUES TONDRA
JO SPADILIERE

Arr. by HENRY COLEMAN

1. En ce jour le so-leil se lè - - ve Et no-tre Con-go res-plen-dit. U - ne lon-gue nuit s'a-chè - ve, Un grand bon-heur a sur-gi. Chan-tons tous a-vec i-vres-se le chant de la li-ber-té.

2. Des fo-rêts jus-qu'à la sa-va-ne, Des sa-va-nes jus-qu'à la mer, Un seul peuple, u-ne seule â-me; Un seul cœur, ar-dent et fier. Lut-tons tous, tant que nous som-mes, pour no-tre vieux pa-ys noir.

★ In 1962 a competition was announced for a National Anthem for CONGO (LÉOPOLDVILLE)

Con-go-lais, de-bout fiè-re-ment par-tout, Pro-cla-mons l'u-nion de no-tre na-tion, Ou-bli-ons ce qui nous di-vi-se, so-yons plus u-nis que ja-mais, Vi-vons pour no-tre de-vi-se: U-ni-té, tra-vail, pro-grès! Vi-vons

pour no - tre de - vi - se: U - ni - té, tra - vail, pro - grès!

3. Et s'il nous faut mourir, en somme
   Qu'importe puisque nos enfants,
   Partout, pourront dire comme
   On triomphe en combattant,
   Et dans le moindre village
   Chantent sous nos trois couleurs.

Translation by T. M. Cartledge

1. On this day the sun rises
   And our Congo stands resplendent.
   A long night is ended,
   A great happiness has come.
   Let us all, with wild joyfulness, sing
   The song of freedom.

CHORUS Arise, Congolese, proud every man,
        Proclaim the unity of our nation.
        Let us forget what divides us
        And become more united than ever.
        Let us live our motto:
        Unity, work, progress.
        Let us live our motto:
        Unity, work, progress.

2. From the forest to the bush,
   From the bush to the ocean,
   One people, one soul,
   One heart, ardent and proud.
   Let us all fight, every one of us,
   For our old black country.

3. And if we have to die,
   What does it really matter? Our children
   Everywhere will be able to say how
   Triumph comes through battle,
   And in the smallest village
   Sing beneath our three colours.

COSTA RICA

Words by
JOSÉ MARIA ZELEDÓN (b. 1877)
(adopted in 1900)
English verses by
MARY ELIZABETH and DICCON SHAW

Music by
MANUEL MARÍA GUTIÉRREZ
(1829-1887)

No - ble pa - tria tu hermo - sa ban - de - ra   ex - pre -
No - ble coun - try, the life   of your peo - ple   Is re -

- sión de tu vi - da nos da: ba - jo el lim - pi - do a-zul de tu
- veal'd in the flag that you fly;   For in peace, white and pure, they live

Adopted as the National Anthem in 1853, when composed.
The first two verses allude to the national flag, of
which the colours are blue, white and red.

cie - lo blan-ca y pu - ra des-can - sa la paz.
tran - quil 'Neath the clear lim - pid blue of your sky.

En la lu - cha te - naz de fe - cun - da la - bor que en - ro-
And their fa - ces are rud - dy with ar - du - ous toil In the

- je - ce del hom - bre la faz, con - qui - sta - ron tus
fields 'neath the life - giv - ing sun. Though your sons are but

hi - jos—la-brie-gos sen-ci - llos— e-ter - no pres-ti - gio, es-ti - ma y ho-
pea - sants, their la-bours e-ter - nal Es-teem,__ re - nown,__ and hon - our have

-nor e - ter - no pres - ti - gio, es - ti - ma y ho - nor.
won, es - teem,— re - nown,— and hon - our have won.

¡Sal-ve, oh tie - - rra gen - til! ¡Sal-ve, oh ma - dre de a-
Hail, oh land of our birth! gra-cious land that we

- mor! Cuan-do al-gu-no pre - ten - da tu glo - ria man-
love! If an en-e-my seek - ing to slan - der you,

- char,— ve - rás a tu pue - blo, va - lien - te y vi-
harms— Your name, then— we will a - ban - don our

G

CUBA

La Bayamesa

Translated by
G. H. HATCHMAN

Versified by
MARTIN SHAW

Words and Music by
PEDRO FIGUEREDO
(1819-1870)

Tempo di Marcia

Al com-ba-te co-rred, ba-ya-
Swift, oh men of Ba-ya-mo, to

Sung for the first time in 1868 during the battle of Bayamo,
in which Figueredo played a leading part.

- me - - ses que la Pa - tria os con - tem - pla or - gu -
bat - - tle! Proud - ly watch - ing, your Moth - er - land ac -

cresc.

- llo - - sa; no te - máis u - na muer - te glo -
-cepts you. Fear not fight - ing to fall; glo - ry

cresc.

- rio - - sa, que mo - rir por la
waits you! For your coun - try to

pp cresc.

Pa - tria es vi - vir. En ca -
die, is to live. To sub -

ff

pp cresc.

CZECHOSLOVAKIA

Part I: Kde Domoj Můj?

Words by
JOSEF KAJETÁN TYL
(1808-1856)

Music by
FRANTIŠEK SAN ŠKROUP
(1801-1862)

This State hymn was officially recognised as the National Anthem in 1919.
It is in two parts. The first is Czech and the second is a Slovak folksong
commemorating the exodus of Slovak students from Bratislavia in 1843.

ráj_____ to na po-hled! A to je ta krá - sná ze - mě, ze-mě

če - ská do-mov můj,___ ze-mě če - ská do-mov můj!

Part 2: Nad Tatrú sa blýská

Words by
JANKO MATÚSKA

Traditional Melody

Allegro energico

Nad Ta - trú sa blý - ská, hro - my di - vo bi - jú,

nad Ta - trú sa blý - ská, hro - my di - vo bi - jú.

Part 1

Where is my home, where is my home?
Streams are rushing through the meadows,
'Mid the rocks sigh fragrant pine groves,
Orchards decked in Spring's array
Scenes of Paradise portray.
And this land of wond'rous beauty
Is the Czech land, home of mine
Is the Czech land, home of mine

Part 2

Lightning strikes our mighty Tatra tempest-shaken,
Lightning strikes our mighty Tatra tempest-shaken.
Stand we fast, friends of mine,
Storms must pass, sun will shine,
Slovaks shall awaken.

DAHOMEY
L'Aube Nouvelle
THE DAWN OF A NEW DAY

Words and music by the
Abbé G. DAGNON
Arr. by HENRY COLEMAN

1. Ja - dis à son ap - pel, nos aï - eux sans fai - bles - se Ont su a - vec cou - rage, ar - deur, pleins d'al - lé - gres - se Li-

Adopted as the National Anthem at the declaration of independence, August, 1960

-vrer au prix du sang des com - bats é - cla - tants. Ac-cou-

-rez vous aus-si, bâ - tis - seurs du pré - sent, Plus forts dans

l'u - ni - té, chaqu' jour à la tâ - che, Pour la

pos - té - ri - té, cons - trui - sez sans re - lâ - che.

CHORUS

En - fants du DA - HO - MEY, de - bout! La li - ber - té d'un cri so - no - re Chante aux pre - miers feux de l'au - ro - re; En - fants du DA - HO - MEY, de - bout!

2. *Quand partout souffle un vent de colère et de haine,*
   Dahoméen, sois fier, et d'une âme sereine,
   Confiant dans l'avenir, regarde ton drapeau!
   Dans le vert tu liras l'espoir du renouveau,
   De tes aïeux le rouge évoque le courage;
   Des plus riches trésors le jaune est le présage.

3. *Tes monts ensoleillés, tes palmiers, ta verdure,*
   Cher DAHOMEY, partout font ta vive parure.
   Ton sol offre à chacun la richesse des fruits.
   DAHOMEY, désormais que tes fils tous unis
   D'un fraternel élan partagent l'espérance
   De te voir à jamais heureux dans l'abondance.

English Paraphrase by
ELIZABETH P. COLEMAN

Chorus

Children of Dahomey, arise!
The resounding cry of freedom
Is heard at the first light of dawn;
Children of Dahomey, arise!

1. Formerly, at her call, our ancestors
   Knew how to engage in mighty battles
   With strength, courage, ardour, and full of joy, but at the price of blood.
   Builders of the present, you too, join forces
   Each day for the task stronger in unity
   Build without ceasing for posterity.

2. When all around there blows a wind of anger and hate:
   Citizen of Dahomey be proud, and in a calm spirit
   Trusting in the future, behold your flag!
   In the green you read hope of spring;
   The red signifies the courage of your ancestors;
   The yellow foretells the richest treasures.

3. Beloved Dahomey, your sunny mountains, palm trees, and green pastures
   Show everywhere your brightness;
   Your soil offers everyone the richest fruits.
   Dahomey, from henceforth your sons are united
   With one brotherly spirit sharing the hope of seeing you
   Enjoy abundance and happiness for ever.

DENMARK
Kong Kristian

Words by
JOHANNES EWALD (1743-1781)
English versification by
H. W. LONGFELLOW
(1807-1882)

Music by
D. L. ROGERT (?)
(1742-1813)
This is not certain.

★Kong Kri - stian stod ved høj - en Mast i røg og
King Christ - ian stood by the loft - y mast In mist and

damp. Hans vær - ge ham - re - de så fast, at
smoke; His sword was ham - mer - ing so fast, Through

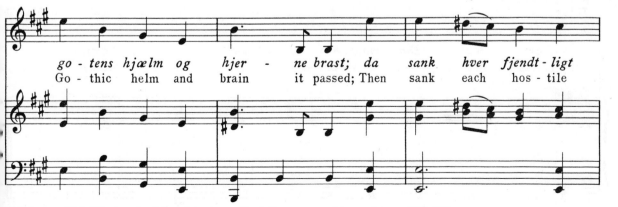

go - tens hjælm og hjer - ne brast; da sank hver fjendt - ligt
Go - thic helm and brain it passed; Then sank each hos - tile

This is the official National and Royal Anthem. Music first appeared in ms. form c.1762-1777;
words first used in the ballad opera *The Fishermen* 1780. There are other verses.
★ King Christian IV (1577-1648) was one of Denmark's great patriotic leaders.

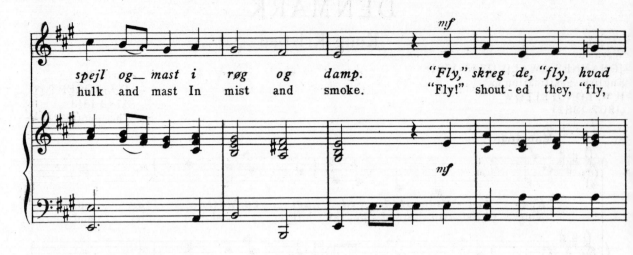

spejl og_ mast i røg og damp. "Fly," skreg de, "fly, hvad
hulk and mast In mist and smoke. "Fly!" shout-ed they, "fly,

flyg - te kan! Hvo står for Dan - marks Kri - sti - an, hvo
he who can! Who braves of Den - mark's Christ - i - an; Who

står for Dan - marks Kri - sti - an i kamp?"
braves of Den - mark's Christ-i - an The stroke?"

DENMARK

Der er et yndigt land

Words by
ADAM GOTTLOB OEHLENSCHLÄGER(1779-1850)
Translated by
CHARLES BRATLI

Music by
HANS ERNST KRØYER
(1798-1879)

Also used on national occasions. Written c. 1819. Its popularity as a national song dates from 4th July, 1844, when students sang it at a national festal meeting to a gathering of 12,000 Danes.

det bug - ter sig i bak - ke, dal, det
It waves from val - ley up to hill, Its

hed - der gam - le Dan - mark, og det er Frej - as
name is old - en Den - mark, And here dwells Frey - a

sal,___ og det er Frej - - as sal.
still,___ And here dwells Frey - - a still.

DOMINICAN REPUBLIC

Words by
EMILIO PRUD'HOMME
English versification by
J. E. HALES and
MARY ELIZABETH SHAW

Music by
JOSÉ REYES (1835-1905)

Quis-que-ya - nos va - lien - tes, al -
Va - liant sons of Quis-que - ya, our

-ce - mos nues-tro can - to_ con vi - va e - mo - ción, Y_ del
chor - us, Let us, heart-felt_ and strong, sing to the world; While, de-

First sung as National Anthem in 1900. Quisqueya is the native name of the island of Santo Domingo.

By permission of J. B. Cramer & Co. Ltd.

H

mun-do_a la faz os-ten-te — mos nues-tro_in-vic-to_glo-rio-so-pen-
-fi — ant and daunt-less, be-fore us We will flou-rish our stan-dard un-

-dón. ¡Sal-ve_el pue-blo que,in tré-pi-do_y fuer-te, a la
furled. Hail! O peo-ple in-tre-pid and dar — ing, Who with

gue-rra_a mo-rir se lan-zó. Cuan-do_en bé-li-co re-to de
ea-ger-ness sprang to at-tack; And, of blood-shed and dan-ger un-

muer — te sus ca-de-nas de_es-cla-vo rom-
-car — ing, Saw the fet-ters of sla-ve-ry

-pió.
crack.

Nin-gun pue - blo ser li - bre me -
Un - de - serv - ing of free - dom the

-re - ce si es es - cla - vo_in do-len - te y ser - vil: Si en su
na - tion Which in ty - ran-ny's bond tame - ly lives, And is

pe - cho la lla - ma no cre - ce que tem -
lack - ing the fine in - spi - ra - tion That from

-pló el he - ro - is - mo vi - ril. Mas Quis - que - ya la in-dó - mi - ta y
true vi - rile cour - age de - rives. But the sons of Quis-que - ya ne'er

bra - va Siem-pre al - ti - va la fren - te al - za -
fail her, And her head car - ried high shall re -

-rá: Que si fue - re mil ve - ces es -
-main; Though a thou - sand times foes should as -

-cla - va O - tras tan - tas ser li - bre sa - brá.
-sail her, She her free - dom would e - ver re - gain.

ECUADOR

Words by
JUAN LEÓN MERA
(1832-1894)
English versification by
T. M. CARTLEDGE

Music by
ANTONIO NEUMANE
(1818-1871)

Officially recognized as the National Anthem by a government decree in 1948.
It had been in use for a considerable time before. The author, in his later years, was President of the Senate of Ecuador.

VERSE

Los pri - mo - ros los hi - jos del sue - lo que so -
Com - ing first were the sons of the coun - try Which Pi -

- ber - bio, el Pi - chin - cha de - co - ra Te a - cla -
- chin - cha on high is a - dorn - ing, Who ac -

- ma - ron por siem - pre se - ño - ra Y ver -
- claimed you as their sov' - reign la - dy And shed

- tie - ron su san - gre por ti Dios mi -
blood for the sake of the land: God look'd

ró y a - cep - tó el ho - lo - ca - - us - to Ye - sa,
on and ac - cept - ed the sa - - cri - fice, And that

san - gre fue ger - men fe - cun - - do De o - tros
blood_ was_ seed_ pro - li - - fic; Oth - er

hé - roes que a - tó - ni - to el mun - - do Vió en tu
her - oes the world ob - served, as - tound - - ed, For the

tor - no a mi - lla - res sur - gir.
fight rise___ up - on ev - 'ry hand.

Dios mi-
God look'd

2

-gir.
hand.

a mi - lla - res sur-
rise___ up - on ev - 'ry

-gir,
hand.

a mi - lla - res sur-gir.
rise up-on ev - 'ry hand.

D.S. al Fine

ÉIRE (IRELAND)
Amhrán na bhFiann
THE SOLDIER'S SONG

Words by
PEADAR KEARNEY (c.1909)

Music by
PEADAR KEARNEY and PATRICK HEANEY
Arr. by T. M. CARTLEDGE

Tempo di Marcia — VERSE

1. *Seo dhíbh, a—cháir - de du-an Óg-láigh, Cath-réim-each bríogh-mhar ceol—mhar, Ár dtein-te—cnámh go bu-a-cach táid, 'San spéir go mín réal-tó-gach, Is*

1. We'll sing a—song, a soldier's song, With cheer-ing, rous-ing cho-rus, As round our—blaz-ing fires we throng, The star-ry heav-ens o'er us; Im-

By permission of Minister of Finance, Éire.
Chorus adopted as Irish National Anthem, July 1926

fonn - mhar faobh - rach— sinn chun gleo, 'S go tiún - mhar glé roimh
-pa - tient for— the — com - ing fight, And as we wait the

cresc. *f*

thiocht do'n ló, Fé chiú - nas— chaomh na hoí - che ar— seol: Seo libh,
morn - ing's light,— Here in the si - lence of— the— night, We'll

cresc. *f*

CHORUS

can-aidh Amh-rán na bhFiann. Sinn - ne Fian - na Fáil A -
chant a sol - dier's song. Sol - diers are we, Whose

-tá fé gheall ag Éir - inn, Buidhean dár sluagh Thar
lives are pledged to Ire - land; Some have come From a

tuinn do ráin-ig chúghainn, Fé —— mhóid bheith saor. Sean-
land be-yond the wave. Sworn — to be free, No

-tír ár sinn-sear feas - ta Ni fág - far fé'n tio-rán ná fé'n
more our an-cient sire - land Shall shel - ter the des-pot or the

tráil. A - nocht a thé-am sa — bheár - na bhaoghail, Le
slave. To - night we man — the — bear - na baoghail In

gean ar Ghaedhil chun báis nó saoghail, Le gun - a - sgréach, fé
Er - in's cause, come woe or weal; 'Mid can - nons' roar and

lámhach na — bpiléar, Seo libh, can-aidh Amh-rán na bhFiann.
ri — fles'— peal We'll chant a sol - dier's song.

2. *Cois bánta réidhe, ar árdaibh sléibhe,*
   Ba bhuadhach ár sinnsear romhainn,
   Ag lámhach go tréan fé'n sár-bhrat séin
   Tá thuas sa ghaoith go seolta.
   Ba dhúthchas riamh d'ár gcine cháidh
   Gan iompáil siar ó imirt áir,
   'S ag siubhal mar iad i gcoinnibh námhad
   Seo libh, canaidh Amhrán na bhFiann.

   CURFÁ: *Sinn-ne Fianna Fáil, etc.*

3. *A bhuidhean nách fann d'fhuil Ghaoidheal is Gall,*
   Sin breacadh lae na saoirse,
   Tá sgeimhle 's sgannradh i gcroidhthibh namhad,
   Roimh ranngaibh laochra ár dtíre.
   Ár dteinte is tréith gan spréach anois,
   Sin luisne ghlé san spéir anoir,
   'S an bíodhbha i raon na bpiléar agaibh:
   Seo libh, canaidh Amhrán na bhFiann.

   CURFÁ: *Sinn-ne Fianna Fáil, etc.*

2. In valley green, on towering crag,
   Our fathers fought before us,
   And conquered 'neath the same old flag
   That's proudly floating o'er us.
   We're children of a fighting race,
   That never yet has known disgrace,
   And as we march, the foe to face,
   We'll chant a soldier's song.

   CHORUS: Soldiers are we, etc.

3. Sons of the Gael! Men of the Pale!
   The long watched day is breaking;
   The serried ranks of Inisfail
   Shall set the Tyrant quaking.
   Our camp fires now are burning low;
   See in the east a silv'ry glow,
   Out yonder waits the Saxon foe,
   So chant a soldier's song.

   CHORUS: Soldiers are we, etc.

EL SALVADOR

Words by
JUAN J. CAÑAS (1826-1912)
English versification by
MARY ELIZABETH
AND DICCON SHAW

Music by
JUAN ABERLE

This was written in 1879 and adopted as the National Anthem in 1953
General Juan Cañas was a diplomat and soldier; at one time Minister of Foreign Affairs.
English words copyright J.B. Cramer & Co. Ltd.

su - yos po-der - nos lla - mar_____ Y ju-
name_____ of thy chil - dren we bear,_____ And with

-re - mos la vi-da a-ni - mo-sos Sin des-
bold and un-tir - ing de - vo - tion To thy_____

can - so a su bien con - sa-grar.
ser - vice our lives let us swear.

Sa - lu -
Moth - er

-de - mos la Pa - tria or - gu - llo - sos De hi - jos
coun - try, thy peo - ple sa - lute thee! Proud - ly the

su - llos po - der - nos lla - mar___ Y ju -
name___ of thy chil - dren we bear,___ And with

-re - mos la vi - da a - ni - mo - sos Sin des -
bold and un - tir - ing de - vo - tion to thy___

-can - so a su bien___ con - sa - grar
ser - vice our lives___ let us swear.

I

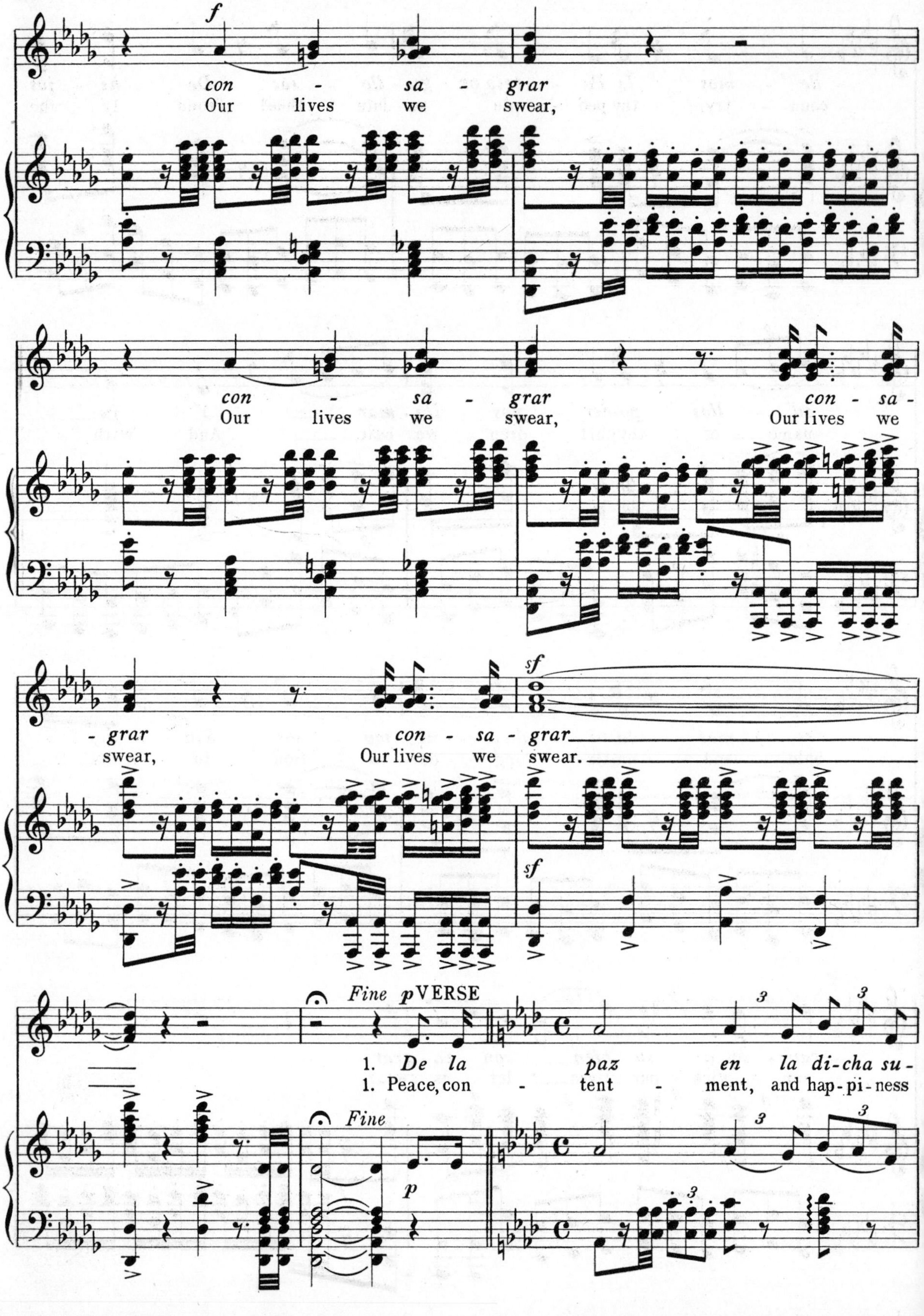
f
con - sa - grar
Our lives we swear,
con - sa - grar con - sa -
Our lives we swear, Our lives we
-grar con - sa - grar
swear, Our lives we swear.
sf
sf
Fine p VERSE
1. De la paz en la di-cha su -
1. Peace, con - tent - ment, and hap-pi-ness
Fine
p

-pre — ma Siem-pre no - ble___ so-ñó El Sal-va dor___ Fué ob-te-
ev — er Was the con-stant dream_ of El_ Sal - va - dor; To a-

-ner — — la su e - ter-no pro - ble — — ma, Con - ser-
-chieve it was her glor-ious am - bi — — -tion, And to

-var — la es su glo — ria ma - yor. Y con
keep___ it for ev — — -er - more. For with

fé in-que-bran-ta - ble el ca - mi — no___ Del pro-
ea - ger faith which nev - er shall fal - ter___ Towards the

124

cho - - - que de ruin des-leal - tad   Des - de el
ram_____ part of steel has with-stood   Since the

dí - - - a que en su alta ban - de - - - ra   Con su
day_____ when a - loft on her stan - - - dard   She wrote

san - gre es-cri - bió_____ li-ber - tad!_____ es - cri - bió_____ li-ber-
"Free - dom" in let - ters of blood_____ She wrote "Free - dom" in

D.C. al Fine

tad!_____ es - cri - bió_____ li - ber - tad!
let - ters, in let - ters of blood.

D.C. al Fine

Ped.   ✱

CORO *Saludemos la patria orgullosos*
De Hijos suyos podernos llamar;
Y juremos la vida animosos,
Sin descanso a su bien consagrar.

2. *Libertad es su dogma, es su guia,*
Que mil veces logró defender;
Y otras tantas de audaz tirania
Rechazar el odioso poder.
  Dolorosa y sangrienta es su historia,
Pero excelsa y brillante a la vez,
Manantial de legitima gloria,
Gran lección de espartana altivez.
  No desmaya su innata bravura:
En cada hombre hay un héroe inmortal,
Que sabrá mantenerse a la altura
De su antiguo valor proverbial.

3. *Todos son abnegados y fieles*
Al prestigio del bélico ardor,
Con que siempre segaron laureles
De la Patria salvando el honor.
  Respetar los derechos extraños
Y apoyarse en la recta razón
Es para ella, sin torpes amaños,
La invariable, más firme ambición.
  Y en seguir esta linea se aferra,
Dedicando su esfuerzo tenaz
En hacel cruda guerra a la guerra;
Su ventura se encuentra en la paz.

CHORUS Mother country, thy people salute thee!
Proudly the name of thy children we bear,
And with bold and untiring devotion
To thy service our lives let us swear.

2. Never tiring, her people have battled
To preserve and guard their liberty:
And with valour have a thousand times over
Broken the powers of base tyranny.
For, though brilliant and sublime is her story,
Yet it tells of her blood and her suffering beside,
And in this is revealed her true glory
And her noble and stoical pride.
All her sons shall be heroes immortal;
They are daring, resourceful, and bold;
For their bravery is a tradition
And they fight like their fathers of old.

3. They will follow this ancient tradition
Which has won for them undying fame
Since with ardour, self-denying and faithful,
They kept spotless their Motherland's name.
Her ambition is firm and unchanging,
To respect and observe others' rights is her pride;
To maintain ever pure the fount of justice
Where uprightness and trust are allied.
She will follow this path with devotion
And with courage which never shall cease;
For, although she gives battle for battle,
Her most fervent desire is for peace.

ESTONIA

Words by
JOHANN WOLDEMAR JANSSEN (1819-1900)

Music by
FREDRIK PACIUS (1809-1891)
Arr. by
HENRY COLEMAN

Maestoso con entusiasmo

Mu i - sa - maa, mu õnn ja rõõm, Kui kau - nis o - led sa! Ei lei - a mi - na ii - al teal See suu - re lai - a ___ il - ma peal, Mis mull' nii ar - mas o - leks ka Kui sa mu i - sa - maa!

First acknowledged as Estonia's National Anthem c.1917. Sung for first time at National Singing Festival, 1st July, 1869
The tune is the same as that of Finland's National Anthem.
The National Anthem of the U.S.S.R. is now used inside Estonia.

2. Sa oled mind ju sünnitand
   Ja üles kasvatand;
   Sind tänan mina alati
   Ja jään sul truuks surmani!
   Mul kõige armsam oled sa,
   Mu kallis isamaa!

3. Su üle Jumal valvaku,
   Mu armas isamaa!
   Ta olgu sinu kaitseja
   Ja võtku rohkest' õnnista'
   Mis iial ette võtad sa,
   Mu kallis isamaa!

Translation by Jenny Wahl

1. My native land, my joy, delight,
   How fair thou art and bright;
   And nowhere in the world all round
   Can ever such a place be found
   So well beloved as I love thee,
   My native country dear!

2. My little cradle stood on thy soil,
   Whose blessings ease my toil.
   With my last breath my thanks to thee,
   For true to death I'll ever be
   O worthy, most beloved and fine,
   Thou, dearest country mine!

3. May God in Heaven thee defend,
   My best, my dearest land!
   May He be guard, may He be shield,
   For ever may He bless and wield
   O graciously all deeds of thine,
   Thou dearest country mine!

ETHIOPIA

Words by a group of
ETHIOPIANS (1930)
English versification by
SEBASTIAN SHAW

Music by
K. NALBANDIAN
(1925)

Moderato

mf E - thi - o - pia hoy Dess - yi - be - lish Be - am - la-
Hail E - thi - o - pia, land e - lect! The pow - er of

-kish hail Be - ne - goo___ sish Te - ba - - be - re - wal___
God your King di - rect___ Your va - liant___ war - riors, in___

ar - ban - yo - tchish A - yen - ne - kam___ ket - to
un - ion se - lect, Their dear land's lib - er -

First performed at the coronation of Haile Selaisse I. 2nd November, 1930

ne - tasn - ne - tish. *Ber* - *too* *na* - *tche* -
-ty to pro - tect. They from moun - tain

-wuna te - ra - ro - tchish *A* - *ti* - *fé* - *rim.* *Ke* - *te* - *la* -
strong-holds shall ef - fect Your foes' down - fall; fear they re-

-to - tchish *Del* *ad* - *ra* - *gi* - *wu* *ne* - *goo* - *sa* - *tchin*
-ject. May our vic - tor - i - ous and great King

Yi - *noo* - *rel* - *len* *le* - *keb* - *ra* - *tchin.*
Live for long and new glo - ry bring.

FAROE ISLANDS
Tú alfagra land mítt

Words by
SÍMUN av SKARÐI
English translation by
C. NISSEN

Music by
PETER ALBERG (1907)
Arr. by HENRY COLEMAN

1. Tú al - fagr - a land mítt, mín dýr - ast - a ogn! Á
vetr - i - so rand - hvítt, á sumr - i við logn, tú
tek - ur meg at tær, so tætt í tín favn. Tit

2. *Hin roðin, sum skínur*
   á sumri í líð;
   hin ódnin, sum týnir
   mangt lív vetrartíð,
   og myrkrið, sum fjalir
   mær bjartasta mál,
   og ljósið, sum spælir
   mær sigur í sál:
   alt streingir, ið tóna,
   sum vága og vóna,
   at eg verji Føroyar, mítt land!

3. *Eg nígi ti niður*
   í bøn til tín, Gud:
   Hin heilagi friður
   mær falli í lut!
   Lat sál mína tváa
   sær í tíni dýrd!
   So torir hon vága,
   – av Gudi væl skírd –
   at bera tað merki,
   sum eyðkennir verkið,
   ið varðveitir Føroyar, mítt land!

Free Translation

1. Oh, Faroe Islands, my dearest treasure!
   When winter storms roar, in warm summer night,
   You draw out yonder my home in your embrace.
   You Islands so graceful, God bless the name
   That our forefathers gave you when beyond the ocean they found you.
   Yes, God bless the Faroe Islands, my land.

2. That sun gleam which hovers round summer green time
   And the storm which claims so many a life in winter;
   The darkness which hides my mountain range and peak
   And the light which billows and whispers in the mind,
   Are strings which vibrate and secretly compel me
   To guard you, Faroe Islands, my country!

3. My knee I will bend in prayer to you, God,
   Your peace, Oh Thou highest, as a message to me bring!
   My soul will bow at your baptismal blessing
   Then it may venture, I hope, with frankness and joy
   To carry forward the mark which witnesses the task
   That serves you, Faroe Islands, my land!

FINLAND

Maamme

OUR LAND

Words by
JOHAN LUDVIG RUNEBERG (1804-1877)

Translated by
CHARLES WHARTON STORK

Music by
FREDRIK PACIUS (1809-1891)

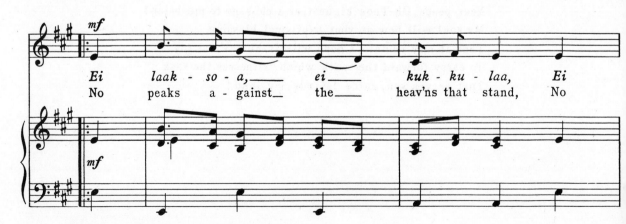

This Anthem was written by Finland's National Poet
Sung for the first time at a students' gathering, 13th May 1848.

cresc.

vet - tä, ran - taa___ rak-kaam-paa, Kuin ko - ti-maa tää poh-joi -
gen - tle dales or___ foam-ing strand are lov'd as we our home re -

ff

- nen, Maa kal - lis i - si - en!
- vere, The earth our sires held dear.

cresc.

ff

2. *Sun kukoistukses kuorestaan*
   Kerrankin puhkeaa!
   Viel' lempemme saa nousemaan
   Sun toivos, riemus loistossaan,
   Ja kerran laulus, synnyinmaa,
   Korkeemman kaiun saa!

2. The flowers in their buds that grope
   Shall burst their sheaths with spring;
   So from our love to bloom shall ope
   Thy gleam, thy glow, thy joy, thy hope,
   And higher yet some day shall ring
   The patriot song we sing!

FRANCE
La Marseillaise

English translation of first verse by
PERCY BYSSHE SHELLEY (1792-1822)
of second verse by
MARY ELIZABETH SHAW

Words and Music by
CLAUDE-JOSEPH ROUGET de L'ISLE
(1760 - 1836)

*Shelley has "behold"
Written and composed on 24th April, 1792
Adopted as National Anthem, 15th July, 1795

dard_ sang-lant est le - vé.   En-ten-dez-vous,   dans les cam-
tears_ and hear their_ cries!   Shall hateful ty - rants mis - chief_

- pag - nes   Mu -   gir ces fa-rou - ches sol - dats.   Ils
breed - ing   With   hire - ling_ hosts, a ruf - fian band   Af-

vien - nent jus-que dans nos bras   é - gor - ger   vos fils, vos com-
-fright and de-so-late the land,   While   peace   and li-ber-ty lie

-pag - nes.   Aux ar -   mes ci - toy - ens!   For-
bleed - ing?   To arms, _____ to arms, ye brave!   Th'a-

κ

- mez ___ vos ba-tail-lons, ___ Mar - chons, mar - chons!
- veng - ing sword un-sheathe! ___ March on! march on!

Qu'un sang im - pur ___ A - breu - ve nos sil-lons.
All hearts re - solved ___ on vic - to-ry or death.

D.C.

2. *Amour sacré de la Patrie,*
   Conduis, soutiens nos bras vengeurs.
   Liberté, liberté chérie,
   Combats avec tes défenseurs; (bis)
   Sous nos drapeaux, que la victoire
   Accoure à tes mâles accents;
   Que tes ennemis expirants
   Voient ton triomphe et notre gloire!

   Aux armes citoyens, etc.

2. O sacred love of France, undying,
   Th'avenging arm uphold and guide.
   Thy defenders, death defying,
   Fight with Freedom at their side.
   Soon thy sons shall be victorious
   When the banner high is raised;
   And thy dying enemies, amazed,
   Shall behold thy triumph, great and glorious.

   To arms, to arms, ye brave! etc.

GABON
La Concorde

Words and Music by
GEORGES DAMAS
Arr. by HENRY COLEMAN

Tempo di Marcia

U - ni _____ dans la Con-cor - de et la _____

_ fra - ter - ni - té, _____ E - veil - le-toi Ga - bon, une

au - ro - re se lè - ve, En - cou - ra - ge l'ar - deur qui

vibre et nous sou-lè - ve! ___ C'est en - fin notre es - sor vers la fé-

rall 2nd time

Fine

-li - ci - té. C'est en - fin notre es - sor vers la fé - li - ci - té.

Fine

CHORUS

p dolce

E - blou - is - sant et fier, ___ le jour

su - bli - me monte ___ Pour-chas - sant à ja-mais ___

l'in - jus - tice et la hon - te. Qu'il mon -

-te, monte en - co - re et cal - me nos a -

-lar - mes, Qu'il pro - ne la ver - tu

et re - pous - se les armes.

2   Oui que le temps heureux rêvé par nos ancêtres
    Arrive enfin chez nous, rejouisse les êtres,
    Et chasse les sorciers, ces perfides trompeurs
    Qui semaient le poison et répandaient la peur.

3   Afin qu'aux yeux du monde et des nations amies
    Le Gabon immortel reste digne d'envie,
    Oublions nos querelles, ensemble bâtissons
    L'édifice nouveau auquel tous nous rêvons.

4   Des bords de l'Ocean au cœur de la forêt,
    Demeurons vigilants, sans faiblesse et sans haine!
    Autour de ce drapeau, qui vers l'honneur nous mène,
    Saluons la Patrie et chantons sans arrêt:

Translation by
T.M. CARTLEDGE

Chorus   United in concord and brotherhood,
         Awake, Gabon, dawn is at hand.
         Stir up the spirit that thrills and inspires us!
         At last we rise up to attain happiness.

1   Dazzling and proud, the sublime day dawns,
    Dispelling for ever injustice and shame.
    May it still advance and calm our fears,
    May it promote virtue and banish warfare.

2   Yes, may the happy days of which our ancestors dreamed
    Come for us at last, rejoicing our hearts,
    And banish the sorcerers, those perfidious deceivers
    Who sowed poison and spread fear.

3   So that, in the eyes of the world and of friendly nations,
    The immortal Gabon may maintain her good repute,
    Let us forget our quarrels, let us build together
    The new structure of which we all have dreamed.

4   From the shores of the Ocean to the heart of the forest,
    Let us remain vigilant, without weakness and without hatred!
    Around this flag which leads us to honour,
    Let us salute the Fatherland and ever sing:

GERMANY
Deutschland- Lied

Words by
HEINRICH HOFFMAN VON FALLERSLEBEN (1798-1874)

Music by
JOSEPH HAYDN (1732 -1809)

Ein - ig - keit und Recht und Frei - heit für das

deut - sche Va - ter - land! Da - nach lasst uns al - le

stre - ben brü - der - lich mit Herz und Hand! Ein - ig -

Authorized as Germany's National Anthem on 11 August, 1922. when the first verse of Heinrich von Fallersleben's poem was sung.   In 1950 the Federal Republic adopted the third verse instead as the official words.

cresc.

-keit und Recht und Frei-heit sind des Glück - es Un - ter -

-pfand Blüh im Glan - ze die - ses

Glück- es blü - he___ deut - sches Va - ter - land!

Free Translation

Unity and right and freedom
for the German fatherland;
let us all pursue this purpose
brotherly, with heart and hands.
Unity and right and freedom
are the pawns of happiness.

Bis { Flourish in this blessing's glory
{ flourish, German fatherland

GHANA

Words by
various authors.
Verse 4 is by the composer

Music by
PHILIP GBEHO

Ritmico, con moto

1. Lift high the flag of Ghana The gay star shining in the sky, Bright with the souls of our fathers, Beneath whose shade we'll live and die, we'll live and die. Red for the blood of the heroes in the fight, Green for the
2. We'll live and die for Ghana, Our land of hope for ages to come! Shout it aloud, O Ghana, And beat it out upon the drum, upon the drum! Come from the palm-lined shore, From the broad northern plain, From the

die.

drum!

Officially became the National Anthem in 1957, the year when independence was attained

fruit - ful___ farms of___ our birth - right,___ And
farm and the for - est, The moun - tain and mine,___ Your

linked with these the shin - ing gold - en band That marks the
child - ren sing with an - cient min - strel lore: Free - dom for

rich - ness of our Fa - ther - land,___ And - land.___
ev - er,___ for ev - er, more.___ Your more.___

D.C.

3. This be our vow, O Ghana,
   To live as one, in unity,
   And in your strength, O Ghana,
   To build a new fraternity!
   Africa waits, in the night of the clouded years,
   For the spreading light that now appears
   To give us all a place beneath the sun,
   The destined ending of a task well done.

4. Lord God, our Father, we pray Thee,
   Be Thou our guide in all our ways.
   May we united together
   Proclaim the dawn of our new day.
   Children of Ghana, arise and uphold your cause,
   And spread the news of Freedom far and wide;
   O God our Father hearken to our call,
   And grant us peace here in our Fatherland.

GREAT BRITAIN

God Save The Queen

Origin of both words and melody obscure.
Earliest copy of words in Gentleman's Magazine, 1745.

2. O Lord our God arise,
    Scatter her enemies,
    And make them fall:
    Confound their politics,
    Frustrate their knavish tricks,
    On Thee our hopes we fix:
    God save us all.

3. Thy choicest gifts in store,
    On her be pleased to pour;
    Long may she reign:
    May she defend our laws,
    And ever give us cause
    To sing with heart and voice
    God save the Queen.

GREECE

Words by
DIONYSIOS SOLOMÓS (1798-1857)

English versification by
T. M. CARTLEDGE

Music by
NIKOLAOS MANTZAROS (1795-1873)

Chosen as National Anthem of Greece by King George I and adopted in 1864.
Of the 158 verses, the first two which are given are those usually sung.

kok - ka-la vyal-me - nee ton el-lee - non ta ye
Greeks of old whose dy - ing Brought to birth our spi - rit

ra _____ Ke san prawt' an - three - o -
free. _____ Now, with an - cient val - our

- me - nee hye-r'o hye - ri e - lef - the - rya. _____ Ke san
ris - ing, Let us hail you, oh Li - ber - ty! _____ Now, with

prawt' an - three - o - me - nee hye - r'o hye r'e - lef - the -

an - cient val - our ris - ing, Let us hail you, Li - ber-

-rya, _____ Ke san prawt' an - three - o -

-ty, _____ Now, with an - cient val - our

-me - nee hye - r'o hye - r'e - lef - the - rya. _____

ris - ing, Let us hail you, Li - ber - ty! _____

GREENLAND

nangminek erinalik

Words by
HENRIK LUND (1875-1948)

Music by
JONATHAN PETERSEN (1881-1961)
Arr. by HENRY COLEMAN

1. nu- nar- put, u- tor- kar- ssu- á- ngo- ra- vit ni ar- kut- u- lig- si- ma- vok kî- nik! kî- tor- na- tit kiv- ssu- mi- -ái- nar- pa- tit, tu- niv- dlu- git si- ne- ri- a- vit pî- nik!

2. akugdlekutaussutut merdlertutut
ilingne perortugut tamâne
kalâtdlinik ingminik taiumavugut
niarkuvit atarkinartup sâne!

3. atortitdlugitdlo tamaisa pisit
ingerdlaniarusulekaugut
nutarterdlugitdlo nokitsigissatit
sujumut, sujumut piumakaugut

This is Greenland's National Song. The Danish National Anthem is also used.

4. *inersimalersut ingerdlanerat*
   tungâlítiterusuleκârput
   oκautsit »avîsit« κanoκ kingunerat
   atúsassoκ erinigileκârput.

5. *taκigdlune nâme atúngiveκaoκ,*
   kâlátdlit, sujumut makigitse!
   inugtut inûneκ pigiuminaκaoκ
   saperase isumaκaleritse!

Free Translation

1. Our immemorial land under the beacon of gleaming ice
   With glowing snow hair around your head !
   You faithful mother, who carried us in your embrace,
   While ocean game of your coasts you promised us.

2. As immature children we have sprung from your soil
   And grown up with you among your mountains .
   Our name is Kalatdlit, in the deep track of legend
   Venerated for the age of its white countenance.

3. And all the while your wealth was used for our good,
   We longed for the new forms of the world :
   Released from the tight bands in the homeland circle
   Now advance; forward towards distant objects we rush.

4. You grown-up nations, stretch out your hand !
   Your track we long soon to follow .
   A world of books shall urge forward the spirit
   Which carries us up on the wave of new learning.

5. Impossible now to tarry inactive longer
   Kalatdlit, stand up! Meet the new day!
   As free-born beings from now on we will grow,
   Begin to have faith in the dawn of ability!

GUATEMALA

Words by
JOSÉ JOAQUÍN PALMA(1844-1911)
Translated by
JOSÉ P. UGARTE
Versified by
MARTIN, MARY ELIZABETH and DICCON SHAW

Music by
RAFAEL ÁLVAREZ (b.1858)

Adopted by governmental decrees of 28 October,1896 and 19 February, 1897, and modified by decree of 26 July,1934
By permission of J.B.Cramer & Co.Ltd.

L

VERSE

¡Gua - te - ma - la fe - liz! que tus a - ras no pro-
Gua - te - ma - la, blest land, home of hap - py race, May thine

-fa - ne ja - más el ver - du - go; ni ha - ya es - cla - vos que la - man el
al - tars pro - fa - ned be nev - er; No yoke of sla - ver - y weigh on thee

yu - go ni ti - ra - nos que es - cu - pan tu faz. Si ma-
e - ver, Nor may ty - rants e'er spit in thy face. Should to-

-ña - na tu sue - lo sa - gra - do lo_a-me - na-za in-va - sión ex-tran-
mor-row see me-naced thy sa - cred soil By in - va-ders all pi - ty de-

-je - ra, li - bre al vien - to tu her-mo - sa ban-
-ny - ing, Your loved flag to the winds free - ly

-de - ra a ven-cer o a mo-rir lla-ma-rá.
fly - ing Will call you to con-quer or die.

GUINEA

Liberté

No words

Music by
ALFA YAYA
Arr. by KEITA FODÉBA
and J. CELLIER

HAITI
La Dessalinienne

Words by
JUSTIN LHÉRISSON
English versification by
MARTIN SHAW
(First verse by
DICCON SHAW and MARY ELIZABETH SHAW)

Music by
NICOLAS GEFFRARD

This anthem was composed for the centenary of national independence in 1903. The title is derived from Jean-Jacques Dessalines, the founder of Haiti as an independent republic, of which he crowned himself Emperor.

2. *Pour les Aïeux*
    Pour la Patrie
    Bêchons joyeux:
    Quand le champ fructifie
    L'âme se fortifie
    Bêchons joyeux
    Pour les Aïeux,
    Pour la Patrie.

3. *Pour le Pays*
    Et pour nos Pères
    Formons des Fils.
    Libres, forts et prospères,
    Toujours: nous serons frères,
    Formons des fils
    Pour le Pays
    Et pour nos Pères.

4. *Pour les Aïeux*
    Pour la Patrie
    O Dieu des Preux!
    Sous ta garde infinie
    Prends nos droits, notre vie,
    O Dieu des Preux!
    Pour les Aïeux,
    Pour la Patrie.

5. *Pour le Drapeau*
    Pour la Patrie,
    Mourir est beau!
    Notre passé nous crie:
    Ayez l'âme aguerrie!
    Mourir est beau
    Pour le Drapeau,
    Pour la Patrie.

2. For sacred soil,
    For sires of old
    We gladly toil.
    When teem field and wold
    The soul is strong and bold.
    We gladly toil, we gladly toil
    For sacred soil,
    For sires of old.

3. For land we love
    And sires of old
    We give our sons.
    Free, happy, and bold,
    One brotherhood we'll hold.
    We give our sons, we give our sons
    For land we love
    And sires of old.

4. For those who gave
    For country all,
    God of the brave,
    To thee, O God, we call;
    Without thee we must fall,
    God of the brave, God of the brave.
    For those who gave
    For country all.

5. For flag on high
    For Native land
    'Tis fine to die.
    Our traditions demand
    Be ready, heart and hand,
    'Tis fine to die, 'tis fine to die
    For flag on high,
    For Native land.

HONDURAS

Words by
AUGUSTO C. COELLO (1881-1941)
English versification by
J. E. HALES
(From the translation by
Señor TIBURCIO CARIAS h,)

Music by
CARLOS HARTLING
(1875-1919)

Tempo di Marcia
con energia

Tu ban-de — ra, tu ban-de — — ra es un
As your stan — dard, as your stan — — dard serves a

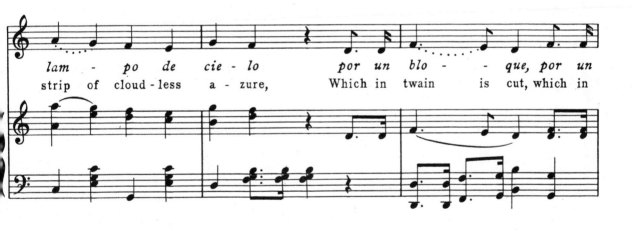

lam — po de cie - lo   por un blo - - que, por un
strip of cloud-less a - zure,   Which in twain is cut, which in

blo — que de— nie - ve cru - za - do;   y se
twain is cut by a band that snows be - sprin - kle;   In whose

This anthem was selected as result of a public competition. It was adopted as the National Anthem in 1915.

By permission of J.B.Cramer & Co.Ltd.

ven   en su fon - do sa - gra - do   cin - co es -
sa - cred   ab - yss - es   there twin - kle   Five pale

- tre - llas de pá - li - do a - zul;   en tu em -
stars   lit with soft - est rays of _ blue.   And   in your

- ble - ma que un mar ru - mo - ro - so   con sus
shield, that   a   stri - dent sea is guard - ing   With the

on - das bra - ví - as es - cu - - da,   De un vol -
bul - wark of its sav - age bil - lows' might,___   A   vol -

-cán,_____ de un vol - cán_____ tras la
ca - no stands, a vol-ca - - no stands, from whose

ci - ma des - nu - da hay un as - - tro, hay un
lone-ly sum-mit's height_ Comes the bea - con clear, comes the

as - - tro de_ ni - ti - da luz.
bea - con clear, of a star that flash-es there.

Fine

Fine

Meno mosso
p VERSE

In - dia, vir - gen y her-mo - sa dor - mi - as de tus
In - dia, like a fair maid you were sleep - ing To the

p

Ped. Ped. sim.

flu - jo i-de-al de tu en - can - to, la
mar - vels of your love - li - ness en - chant - ed, De

or - la a - zul de tu es-plén - di - do
-vout - ly a kiss love - la - den he im -

man - to con su be - so de a-mor con-sa-gró.
-plant - ed On your man - tle's rich mar - gin of blue.

D.C. al Fine

2.

Por guardar ese emblema divino,
marcharemos Oh Patria a la muerte,
generosa será nuestra suerte,
si morimos pensando en tu amor.—
Defendiendo tu santa bandera
y en tus pliegues gloriosos cubiertos,
serán muchos, Oh Honduras tus muertos,
pero todos caerán con honor.—

2.

In defence of our glorious emblem
We are ready, my Country, to perish,
For future ages their fame will ever cherish
Who in their dying hour are thinking of your love.
In the defence of your holy banner fallen,
Their lifeless forms in its hallowed folds enshrouded.
Not few, blessed Honduras, shall be your proud dead,
But they all in honour's cause will die.

HUNGARY

Words by
FERENC KÖLCSEY (1790-1838)

Music by
FERENC ERKEL (1810-1893)
Arr. by HENRY COLEMAN

Ferenc Erkel was the creator of the Hungarian romantic Grand Opera. From 1875-1886 he was Director of the National Academy of Music, and he founded in 1867 the National Association of Hungarian Choirs.

This was awarded first prize in a national competition in 1844 when it was officially adopted.

ICELAND
Lofsöngur

Words by
MATTHIAS JOCHUMSSON (1835-1920)

Music by
SVEINBJÖRN SVEINBJÖRNSSON
(1847-1926)

Ó, guð vors lands, ó, lands vors guð, vjer lof-um þitt heil-ag-a, heil-ag-a nafn. Úr sól-kerf-um himn-ann-a knýt-a þjer kranz þín-ir her-skar-ar, tím-ann-a safn. Fyr-ir þjer er einn dag-ur sem þús-und ár, og

Written and composed in 1874, when Iceland secured its own constitution and also celebrated the one thousandth anniversary of the first permanent settlers of Europeans (Norwegians) on the island.

þús - und ár dag - ur, ei meir,   eitt ei - lífð-ar smá blóm með

titr - and-i tár, sem til - bið-ur guð sinn og deyr.   Ís-lands

þús - und ár, Ís-lands þús - und ár   eitt ei - lífð-ar smá - blóm með

titr - and-i tár, sem til - bið-ur guð sinn og deyr.

Free Translation

Our country's God! Our country's God!
We worship Thy name in its wonder sublime
The suns of the heavens are set in Thy crown
By Thy legions, the ages of time!
With Thee is each day as a thousand years,
Each thousand of years, but a day.
Eternity's flow'r with its homage of tears,
That reverently passes away.
   Iceland's thousand years!
Eternity's flow'r, with its homage of tears,
That reverently passes away.

INDIA

Jană Gană Mană

Words and melody by
RABINDRANATH TAGORE (1861-1941)
Arr. by BRYSON GERRARD

Maestoso

Ja-nă ga-nă ma-nă ad-hi - ña-ya-ka ja-yă hé! Bhă - ra-tă bha-gyă vi-

dhă - tă. Pan - jă - bă, Sin - dhă, Guj-ră - tă, Ma - hă - ră - ta,

Dra - vi - dă, Ut - ka - lă, Van - gă, Vind - hyă, Hi - mă - cha - lă,

Officially adopted by the Indian Constitutional Assembly on
24th January 1950, two days before the proclamation of the Republic.

172

*See Footnote 2

Ja - yă, ja - yă, ja - yă, ja - yă hé! Bhă - ră - tă bha-gyă vi - dhă - tă.

Free Translation

Thou art the ruler of the minds
of all people,
Thou Dispenser of India's destiny,
Thy name rouses the hearts
of the Punjab, Sind,
Gujrat and Maratha, of Dravid,
Orissa and Bengal.
It echoes in the hills of
the Vindhyas and Himalayas,
Mingles in the music of
Jumna and Ganges,
and is chanted by the waves
of the Indian sea.
They pray for thy blessing
and sing thy praise,
Thou Dispenser of India's destiny,
Victory, Victory, Victory to thee!

*Note 1. It will be noticed that the tune ends on the subdominant. The two bars in small notes at the end are not infrequently added — but they are not part of the original melody.

2. For ordinary performances it is usual to end at the first asterisk.

3. The Bengali words of the song have been transliterated for English readers and should therefore be pronounced as in English, i.e. 'J' as in the English 'John'. 'Hs' should be lightly aspirated, even in 'th' which is pronounced as in 'at home' said rather quickly. 'Sh' and 'ch', however, remain as in English; 'g' is always hard; 'é' as in French.

INDONESIA

Indonesia Raya

Words and Music by
WAGE RUDOLF SUPRATMAN
(1903-1938)

1. In - do - ne - sia___ ta - nah a -
2. In - do - ne - sia!___ Ta - nah jang
3. In - do - ne - sia!___ Ta - nah jang

- ir - ku   Ta - nah tum - pah   da - rah - ku.   Di - sa -
mu - lia,   Ta - nah ki - ta   jang ka - ja.   Di - sa -
su - tji,   Ta - nah ki - ta   jang sak - ti.   Di - sa -

This was adopted as the Nationalist Party Song in 1928, and became the National Anthem in 1949.

178

Free Translation

1 INDONESIA, our native country
   Consecrated with our spilt blood
   Where we all arise to stand guard
   Over this our Motherland:
   Indonesia our nationality
   Our people and our country.
   Come then, let us all demand
   Indonesia united.
   Long live our land
   Long live our state
   Our nation, our people, and all
   Arouse then its spirit,
   Organise its own bodies
   To obtain Indonesia the Great.

2 INDONESIA, an eminent country,
   Our wealthy country
   There we shall be forever.
   Indonesia, the country of our
   ancestors,
   A relic of all of us.
   Let us pray
   For Indonesia's prosperity:
   May her soil be fertile
   And spirited her soul,
   The nation and all the people.
   Conscious be her heart
   And her mind
   For Indonesia the Great.

3 INDONESIA, a sacred country,
   Our victorious country:
   There we stand
   Guarding our true Mother.
   Indonesia, a beaming Country,
   A country we love with all our heart,
   Let's make a vow
   That Indonesia be there forever.
   Blessed be her people
   And her sons,
   All her islands, and her seas.
   Fast be the country's progress
   And the progress of her youth
   For Indonesia the Great.

CHORUS INDONESIA the Great, independent and free,
        My beloved land and country.
        Indonesia the Great, independent and free,
        Long live Indonesia the Great.

IRAN
Imperial Salute

Words by
S. AFSAR
English versification by
FRANCIS GOULDING and T. M. CARTLEDGE
from a translation by MAS'UUD FARZAAD

Music by
Lieut. NAJMI MOGHADDAM

First used about 1934

'uhde baw - se - tan.   Az dush-man-awn   boo-dee par-eesh awn
once used to stand.   Though once be-set   by the foe-men's rage,

Dar saw - ye-yash   aw - soo - de I - rawn.   I - ran - i - awn
Now it has peace   in his keep-ing sure;   We of I - ran, re-

pay-vas - te shaw dawn Ham-var - e yaz dawn Bu-vad oo - ra ne-gah-bawn.
-joice in ev-'ry age.   Oh, may God pro-tect   him both now and ev-er-more.

2. *Ay! Par-chamm-i-khoor-sheed-i-I-rawn*
   Par-to af-kann be roo-yi-een Je-hawn
   Yawd aw-varr az oon roo-ze-gaw-ree
   Kaw-sood az bar-qi-tee-ghat harr ke-rawn.
   Dan saw-yè-yat jawn-mee-fa-shaw-neem
   Az dush-man-awn jawn mee-se-taw-neem
   Maw vaw-ress-i-mul-ki-kay-aw-neem
   Ham-ee-shè khaw-heem vat-tan-naw az del-lo-jawn.

3. *Boo-dee-mo has-teem pai-ru-vi-haqq.*
   Juz haqq harr-gez na-khaw-heem az Je-hawn
   Baw shah-pa-ras-tee mam-li-kat-raw
   Daw-reem az dass-ti-dush-man darr em-awn.
   Maw pai-ru-vi ker-dawr-i-neek-eem
   Ro-shan-dell az pan-daw-ri-neek-eem
   Rakh-shan-dè az goof-taw-ri-neek-eem
   Shoo-dzeen faz-zaw-'el bu-lan-daw vaw-zè I-rawn.

2. Oh, Sun that shines on Iran's banner,
   Shed upon each nation rays strong and fair.
   Those days keep in our recollection
   When thy flashing sword brought peace everywhere.
   We give our lives in thy shade benign,
   And take the lives of each enemy.
   We are the heirs of Kianis' line;
   Oh, belovèd land, ever wholly thine are we.

3. Of Right we've been and still are champions.
   What is right is all we ever demand.
   Through worship of the King, we ever
   From the enemy will guard this our land.
   "Good Deeds" the first virtue of our call,
   "Good Thoughts" the light our hearts and minds to guide,
   And through "Good Speech" shining, one and all,
   This is Iran's fame that will echo far and wide.

IRAQ

No words

Music by
L. ZAMBAKA

Tempo di Marcia

This became the National Anthem in 1959, when it was composed.

ISLE OF MAN

Arrane Ashoonagh Dy Vannin

Words by
WILLIAM HENRY GILL
(1839-1922)

Manx translation by
JOHN J. KNEEN
(1873-1939)

Music adapted by
WILLIAM HENRY GILL
(1839-1922)

from a Traditional Manx Air

1. O__ Hal-loe nyn ghooie, O__ Ch'lie-geen ny s'bwaaie
2. Nyn__ El-lan fo-hee, Cha boir noid-yn ee.
1. O__ land of our birth. O__ gem of God's earth,
2. Our__ Is-land, thus blest, No__ foe can mo lest;

Ry ghed-din er ooir aa-lin Yee! Shickyr ta dty Ard-stoyl,
Nee bis-hagh nyn eeast-yn as grain; Nee'n Chiarn shin y 'reayll
O__ Is-land so strong and so fair; Built firm as Bar-rool,
Our grain and our fish shall in-crease; From bat-tle and sword

Farraght-yn myr Bar-rule, As__ freayll shin ayns seyrs-nys as shee.__
Voish strieughyn yn theill, As__ croo-in-agh lesh shee 'n Ashoon ain.__
Thy__ Throne of Home Rule Makes us free as thy sweet moun-tain air.__
Pro-tect-eth the Lord, And crown-eth__ our na-tion with peace.__

The main National Anthem is that for Great Britain. This anthem was dedicated to The Lady Raglan, 1907. There are 8 verses in all.

W.H.Gill, a keen Manxman, was a collector and arranger of Manx music, of which he made a special study. J. J. Kneen was an expert on the Manx language and author of several books on it. For his scholarship he was awarded the Order of St Olaf by H.M.The King of Norway, in recognition also of the historical connection between Norway and the Isle of Man.

ISRAEL

Hatikvah
THE HOPE

Words by
NAFTALI HERZ IMBER
(1856-1909)

Melody traditional

Hatikva is now firmly established as the Anthem of the State of Israel as well as the Jewish National Anthem

Free Translation

While yet within the heart-inwardly
The soul of the Jew yearns,
And towards the vistas of the East-eastwards
An eye to Zion looks.
'Tis not yet lost, our hope,
The hope of two thousand years,
To be a free people in our land
In the land of Zion and Jerusalem.

ITALY
Inno di Mameli

Words by
GOFFREDO MAMELI
(1827-1849)

Music by
MICHELE NOVARO
(1822-1885)

Adopted as National Anthem 2nd June, 1946, on the
establishment of the Italian Republic.

-tel - li d'I - ta - lia, l'I - ta - lia s'è

de - sta, del - l'el - mo di Sci - pio s'è

cin - ta la te - sta. Do - v'è la vit -

rall.   a tempo

-to - ria? Le por - ga la chio - ma, chè schia - va di

Ro - ma Id - di - o la cre - ò.

Fratel - li d'I - ta - lia, l'I - ta - lia s'è de - sta, dell'el - mo di Sci - pio s'è cin - ta la te - sta. Dov'è la vit- -to - ria? Le por - ga la chio - ma, che schia - va di Ro - ma Iddio la cre-

Free Translation

Italian Brothers,
Italy has arisen,
Has put on the helmet of Scipio.
Where is Victory?
Created by God
The slave of Rome,
She crowns you with glory.
Let us unite,
We are ready to die,
Italy calls.

IVORY COAST
l'Abidjanaise

Words by MATHIEU EKRA
in collaboration with JOACHIM BONY
and the Abbé COTY

Music by the Abbé
PIERRE MICHEL PANGO
Arr. by HENRY COLEMAN

Tempo di Marcia moderato

Sa - lut ô ter - re d'es - pé - ran - ce;
Tes fils____ chére Cote d'I - voi - re

Pa - ys de l'hos - pi - ta - li - té.____ Tes lé - gions rem - plies de vail -
Fiers ar - ti - sans de ta gran - deur,____ Tous ras - sem - blés et pour ta

- lan - ce Ont re - le - vé ta di - gni - té.____
gloi - re Te bâ - ti - ront dans le bon -

This National Anthem was adopted at the declaration of independence on 7th August, 1960
The music was composed by an Ivory Coast priest.
Mathieu Ekra is Minister of Information and Joachim Bony Minister of Education in the Ivory Coast.

à l'hu-ma-ni-té, En for-geant, u - nie dans la

foi nou-vel - le, la pa-trie de la vraie fra-ter-ni - té.

English Paraphrase by
ELIZABETH P. COLEMAN

We salute you, O land of hope, country of hospitality; thy gallant legions have restored thy dignity.

Belovèd Ivory Coast, thy sons, proud builders of thy greatness, all mustered together for thy glory, in joy will construct thee.

Proud citizens of the Ivory Coast, the country calls us. If we have brought back liberty peacefully, it will be our duty to be an example of the hope promised to humanity, forging unitedly in new faith the Fatherland of true brotherhood.

JAMAICA

Words by
The Rev. HUGH SHERLOCK (b.1905)

Music by
ROBERT LIGHTBOURNE
Arr. by MAPLETOFT POULLE

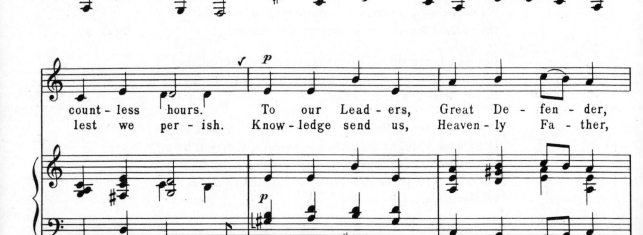

1. E - ter - nal Fa - ther bless our land, Guard us with Thy
2. Teach us true re - spect for all, Stir re - sponse to

Migh - ty Hand, Keep us free from e - vil powers, Be our light through
du - ty's call, Streng-then us the weak to cher-ish, Give us vi - sion

count - less hours. To our Lead - ers, Great De - fen - der,
lest we per - ish. Know - ledge send us, Heaven - ly Fa - ther,

This was officially selected as the National Anthem by the House of Representatives
in Jamaica on 19th July 1962. Robert Lightbourne is a Jamaican and Minister of Trade
and Industry at the time of composing the Anthem. The Rev. Sherlock, a Jamaican, has for
many years been associated with "Boys' Town" in one of the poorer districts of Kingston.

JAPAN

THE PEACEFUL REIGN

Words selected from the
seventh volume of *Kokinshu*
dating from the 9th Century.
English translation by
SAKUZO TAKADA

Music composed by
court musicians and
selected in 1880 by
HIROMORI HAYASHI
Revised by F. ECKERT

Ki - ma - ga - - yo — wa chi - yo - ni:
May Thy peace - ful reign last long! May it last for —

ya - chi - yo - ni sa - za - ré - - i - shi - no i - wa - o to
thou - sands of years, Un - til — this ti - ny stone will grow in - to a

na - re - té ko - ke - no mu - su - ma - - dé.
mas - sive rock And the moss will cov - er it — all deep and thick.

First performed on 3rd November, 1880, on the Emperor Meiji's birthday,
and approved as National Anthem on 12th August, 1893.

JOHORE
Lago Bangsa Johore

Malay words by
Captain H.M. Said BIN H. SULIEMAN S.M.J.
English words by
H.A. COURTNEY

Music by
M. GALISTAN

The music received the Assent of His Highness Sir Abu Bakar,
Maharajah of Johore (afterwards Sultan of Johore) in 1879.
The words received the Assent of His Highness Sir Ibrahim,
Sultan of Johore, in 1915.

Luas - kan kua - sa, Men - aong kan ka - mi, Ra -
Long may his hand, Pro - tect our land, And

- yat di - pim - pi - ni, Ber - ze - man la - gi, Den -
lead his peo - ple on, Through years to be, In

gan mer - deh - ka ber - sa - tu ha - ti All - ah ber - ka - ti Jo - hore,
free - dom and in u - ni - ty God bless Jo - hore,

All - ah sla - mat kan Sul - tan!
God save the Sul - tan!

JORDAN

Words by
Professor 'ABDULMUN 'IM AR-RIFAA'I

Music by
Professor ABDULKADIR AT-TANNIR

'A - sha al Ma - leek   Sa - mi - yan ma - qa - mu - hu

Kha - fi - qa - tin_ fil ma - 'a - li_ a - 'lam - u - hu.

Free Translation

Long live the King
Long live the King
His position is sublime
His banners waving in glory supreme.

Adopted as National Anthem when Emir Abdullah became King, 25 May, 1946.

KOREA

English versification by
JOHN STARR KIM

Music by
EAKTAI AHN

KUWAIT

No words

This is played on ceremonial occasions.

LAOS

Words by
MAHA PHOUMI
English versification by
T. M. CARTLEDGE

Music by
S. E. THONGDY

Xad - lao tang - tè - deum - ma khung - xu - lu -
Once our La - o - tian race in A - sia

-xa you - ney - a - xy Xao - lao pouk - phan - mey -
high - ly hon - oured stood, And at that time the

-try houam - sa - ma - khy hak - ho - hom - kan. Hak-
folk of La - os were u - ni - ted in love. To -

The music is reproduced by permission of Institut fur Auslands-
beziehungen, Stuttgart, from *Die National-Hymnen Der Erde*.
Adopted as National Anthem, 1947. Written and first used 1941.

-xad hak-pa-thet-hao hak-tiao pok-két-ké-
-day they love their race and ral-ly round their

-sa. Hom-hak houam sat-sa-na té-bou-hal-
chiefs, They guard the land and the re-li-gion

-ma hak-sa-din-dèn. Bo hey xad-dey-ma
of their an-ces-tors. They will re-sist each

-louan ra-vi-lop-kouan nhad-nheng-xing ao: Phey-khun-
foe who may op-press them or in-vade And

-khao ma-lou-voun-vay sou-choon-toua-
such in-vad-ers will be met with

-tay tane-thane-sad-trou. Xouy-xeud-xou leuad-neua-xeua-
bat-tle un-to death. They'll re-store the fame of

-phao fun-fou-kou ao ban-hao-thouk-kan.
La-os and through ills u-nit-ed stand.

French Words

Notre race Lao a jadis connu en Asie une grande renommée.
Alors les Lao étaient unis et s'aimaient.
Aujourd'hui encore ils savent aimer leur race et leur pays et se
    groupent autour de leurs chefs.
Ils ont conservé la religion de leurs pères et ils savent garder le
    sol des aïeux.
Ils ne permettront pas que quelque nation vienne les troubler ou
    s'emparer de leur terre.
Quiconque voudrait envahir leur pays les trouverait résolus à
    combattre jusqu'à la mort.
Tous ensemble ils sauront restaurer l'antique gloire du sang lao et
    s'entr'aider aux jours d'épreuves.

LATVIA

Translated by
Dr. GEORGE A. SIMONS

Words and Music by
KARLIS BAUMANIS
(1834-1904)

Dievs,   svē - ti   Lat - vi - ju,   mūs'   dār - go
Bless   Lat - vi - a,   O God,   Our   ver - dant

tē - vi - ju,   svē - ti   jel   Lat - vi - ju,   ak
na - tive sod.   Where   Bal - tic   he - roes trod,___

svē - ti   jel   to !   to !   Kur   lat - vju
Keep   her   from   harm !   harm !   Our   love - ly

Originally written as an entry for a singing festival in 1873, it very soon became the National Anthem
Since 1940 the National Anthem of the U.S.S.R. has been sung inside Latvia.

LEBANON

Words by
RACHID NAKHLÉ

Music by
WADIA SABRA

1. Koul - lou - na   lil - oua - tann Lil -'ou - la   lil 'a
2. Chay - khou - na   oual - fa - ta   in - da - saôu - til   oua
3. Bah - rou - hou   bar - rou - hou Dour - ra - touch - char

Adopted officially by
Presidential decree on 12th July, 1927

lam,   Mil - ou 'ay   niz - za - man Say - fou - na oual ka -
tann   Ous - dou ghâ   bin ma - ta Sa - oua - rat nal - fi -
kain   Kil - dou - hou   bir - rou - hou Ma - li - oul kout -

- lam,   Sah - lou - na oual - ja - bal   man bi
- tann   Char - kou - na kal - bou - hou   a - ba
- baïn   is - mou - hou 'iz - zou - hou moun zou

tonn lir - ri - jâl, Kaou - lou - na oual 'a - mal   Fi - sa
dann loub - nane Sa - na - hou rab bou - hou   Li - ma
kâ - nal jou - doude Maj - dou - hu ar zou - hou   Ram - zou -

-bî - lil ka mâl.
-dal az - mane. Koul - lou - na lil - oua - tann Lil' ou-
-hou lil - khou - loude

-la lil 'a-lam, koul-lou - na lil - oua - tann.

Free Translation

1. All of us! For our Country, for our Flag and Glory!
   Our valour and our writings are the envy of the ages.
   Our mountains and our valleys, they bring forth stalwart men.
   And to Perfection all our efforts we devote.
   All of us! For our Country, for our Flag and Glory!

2. Our Elders and our children, they await our Country's call:
   And on the Day of Crisis they are as Lions of the Jungle.
   The heart of our East is ever Lebanon:
   May God preserve her until end of time.
   All of us! For our Country, for our Flag and Glory!

3. The Gems of the East are her land and sea.
   Throughout the world her good deeds flow from pole to pole.
   And her name is her glory since time began.
   Immortality's Symbol— the Cedar— is her Pride
   All of us! For our Country, for our Flag and Glory!

LIBERIA

Words by
DANIEL BASHER WARNER★

Music by
OLMSTEAD LUCA

Moderato

1. All hail, Li-be-ria, hail! All hail, Li-be-ria,
2. All hail, Li-be-ria, hail! All hail, Li-be-ria,

hail! This glo-rious land of li-ber-ty Shall
hail! In u-nion strong suc-cess is sure— We

long be ours____ Though new her name, Green be her fame, And
can-not fail!____ With God a-bove Our rights to prove We

*Third President of Liberia, 1864-1868

migh - ty be her pow'rs
will o'er all pre - vail!

And migh - ty be her pow'rs
We will o'er all pre - vail!

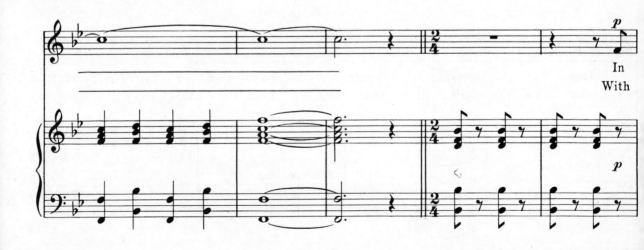

In
With

p

p

joy and glad - ness With our hearts u - ni - ted, We'll shout the
heart and hand Our coun-try's cause de-fend - ing We'll meet the

free - dom Of a race be - night - ed, Long live Li - be - ria,
foe With va - lour un - pre - tend - ing.

hap - py land! A home of glo-rious li - ber-ty, By God's com -

- mand! A home of glo-rious li - ber-ty, By God's com - mand!

LIBYA

Words by
AL BASCHIR AL AREBI

Music by
MOHAMMED ABDUL WAHAB

Alla marcia

CHORUS

Ya Bi-la - di Ya Bi-la - di Bi-ji-ha-di Wa-ji-la -

- di Id-fa-'i Kay-dal A-'a - di Wal-'a-wa - di Was-la-

- mi Is-la-mi Ii-la-mi Is-la-mi Tu-lal Ma-

This National Anthem was written and adopted in 1954,
three years after the attainment of independence.

- *tan* Lib - *ya* Lib - *ya.*

Free Translation

CHORUS

Oh my country! With my struggle and my patience
Drive off enemies and mishaps,
    And survive!
Survive all through
We are your ransom
    Oh Libya!

VERSE

Oh my country! You are the heritage of grandfathers,
May God cast off any hand that would harm you
Do survive! We are for ever your soldiers,
If you survive we care not who perishes.
To you we give solemn pledges
That we, Oh Libya, will never fail you.
    We will never
      Go back to fetters,
We have been liberated, and we have freed our home country
    Libya.

LIECHTENSTEIN

Words by
H. H. JAUCH (1850)

Composer unknown

1. O - ben am deut - schen Rhein leh - net sich Liech - ten-stein
2. Wo einst Sankt Lu - zi - en Frie - den nach Rä - ti - en

an Al - pen - höh'n. Dies lie - be Hei - mat-land im deut - schen
hin - ein ge - bracht, dort an dem Gren - zen-stein und längs dem

Va - ter-land hat Got - tes — wei - se Hand für uns er - seh'n.
jun - gen Rhein steht furcht - los — Liech - ten-stein auf Deutschlands Wacht.

The tune is the same as that of the National Anthem of Great Britain.

3. *Lieblich zur Sommerzeit*
    Auf hoher Alpenweid
    Schwebt Himmelsruh,
    Wo frei die Gemse springt,
    Kühn sich der Adler schwingt,
    Der Senn' das Ave singt
    Der Heimat zu.

4. *Von grüngen Felsenhöhn*
    Freundlich ist es zu sehn
    Mit einem Blick,
    Wie des Rheines Silberband
    Säumet das schöne Land,
    Ein kleines Vaterland
    Voll stillen Glücks.

5. *Hoch lebe Liechtenstein,*
    Blühend am deutschen Rhein,
    Glücklich und treu.
    Hoch leb der Fürst vom Land,
    Hoch unser Vaterland,
    Durch Bruderliebe Band
    Vereint und frei.

Free Translation

1. High above the German Rhine
    leans Liechtenstein
    against Alpine slopes.
    This beloved homeland
    in the German fatherland
    was chosen for us by
    the Lord's wisdom.

3. Lovely in summer-time
    on high Alpine pastures
    floats heavenly peace,
    where the chamois freely jumps about,
    the eagle sways boldy in the air,
    the herdsman sings the 'Ave'
    towards the homeland.

2. Where once St. Lucius
    brought peace to Rätien,
    there on the boundary-stone
    and along the young Rhine
    stands dauntless Liechtenstein
    on Germany's guard.

4. From high green rocks
    it is a lovely sight to watch
    how the silvery ribbon of the Rhine
    edges the beautiful country,
    a small fatherland,
    full of quiet happiness.

5. Long live Liechtenstein,
    blossoming on the German Rhine,
    happy and faithful.
    Long live the Duke of the Land,
    Long live our fatherland,
    united by brotherly bonds and free.

LITHUANIA

Words and Music by
VINCAS KUDIRKA (1858-1899

This became the National Anthem 1918 and first appeared in print in 1896
In Lithuania the National Anthem of the U.S.S.R. is now used.

ša-li-na Ir švie-sa ir tie-sa
šir-dy-se Var-dan tos Lie-tu-vos

mūs žings-nius te-ly-di — vie-ny-bė te-žy-di!

3. *Tegul saulė Lietuvos*
   Tamsumus prašalina,
   Ir šviesa, ir tiesa
   Mūs žingsnius telydi.

4. *Tegul meilė Lietuvos*
   Dega mūsų širdyse,
   Vardan tos Lietuvos
   Vienybė težydi!

1. Lithuania, land of heroes,
   Thou our Fatherland that art,
   From the glorious deeds of ages
   Shall Thy children take heart.

2. May Thy children ever follow
   Their heroic fathers
   In devotion to their country
   And good will to others.

3. May the sun of our loved shore
   Shine upon us evermore;
   May the right and the truth
   Keep our pathway lighted.

4. May the love of our dear land
   Make us strong of heart and hand,
   May our land ever stand
   Peaceful and united.

LUXEMBOURG

Ons Hémécht
OUR MOTHERLAND

Words by
MICHAEL LENTZ
(1820–1893)

Translated by
NICHOLAS E. WEYDERT

Music by
A. ZINNEN
(1827–1898)
Arr. by MARTIN SHAW
(1875–1958)

First performed 5th June, 1864, this became the National Anthem in 1895 replacing
De Feierwon (The Festal Train) by the same author (a well-known poet) and composer.
De Feierwon was written in 1859 to celebrate the opening of the first international
railway system connecting the Grand Duchy with the outside world.   It is still a
popular hymn in Luxembourg.

2. *O Du do uewen, dém seng Hand*
Durch d'Welt d'Natio'ne lêd,
Behitt Du d'Letzeburger Land
Vum friéme Joch a Lêd.
Du hues ons all als Kanner schon
De freie Gêscht jo gin;
LôB viru blénken d'Freihêtssonn,
De' mir 'so' lâng gesin.
LôB viru blénken d'Freihêtssonn,
De' mir 'so' lâng gesin.

2. Oh Father in Heaven Whose powerful hand
Makes states or lays them low,
Protect the Luxembourger land
From foreign yoke and woe.
God's golden liberty bestow
On us now as of yore.
Let Freedom's sun in glory glow
For now and evermore.

MADAGASCAR
O, Our Beloved Fatherland

Words by P. RAHAJASON

Music by
NORBERT RAHARISOA
Arr. by HENRY COLEMAN

This National Anthem was adopted on 21st October, 1958. Madagascar
celebrated the birth of the Malagasay Republic on 26th June, 1960.

CHORUS

-hi - onao ry Za-na-ha - ry 'Ty No - si-ndrazanay i-ty____ Hi - a - da-na sy ho fi - na - ri-tra He sa-mba-tra to-koa i - za-hay____ Ta hay.

1. O, our beloved fatherland,
   O, fair Madagascar,
   Our love will never decay
   But will last eternally.

2. O, our beloved fatherland,
   Let us be thy servant
   With body, heart and spirit
   In dear and worthy service.

3. O, our beloved fatherland,
   May God bless thee,
   That created all lands;
   In order He maintains thee.

CHORUS O, Lord Creator do Thou bless
   This Island of our Fathers
   That she may be happy and prosperous
   For our own satisfaction.

MALAYA
NEGARA KU
MY COUNTRY

Words compiled by
a special Committee

Melody derived from
old Malay folk tune

For short version cut from A to B

Adopted as National Anthem when Malaya achieved Independence
on 31st August, 1957. It was previously known in Malaya and Indonesia as a popular song called Terang Bulan (Moonlight): but this
popular version of the tune is now banned.

kan ___ Ra - ja ki - ta se - la - mat ber - takh -

ta ___ Rah - mat bah - gia tu - han kur - ni - a kan ___

Ra - ja ki - ta se - la - mat ber - takh - ta. ___

Free Translation

My Country,
The land of my birth.
May her people live in unity and prosperity,
May God grant His blessings upon her,
Peacefully may our Ruler reign.
May God grant His blessings upon her,
Peacefully may our Ruler reign.

MALI

Music by
BANZOUMANA SISSOKO
Arr. by HENRY COLEMAN

Alla marcia

A ton ap-pel, MA-LI, Pour ta pros-pé-ri-té Fi-dèle à ton des-tin Nous se-rons tous u-nis, Un peuple, un but, u-ne foi. _____ Pour une A-frique u-nie Si l'én-ne-mi découvre son front Au de-dans ou au de-hors De-bout sur les rem-

This National Anthem was adopted by the National Assembly of Mali on 9th August 1962

parts Nous som - mes ré - so - lus de mou - rir.

Chorus

Pour l'A - frique et pour toi MA - LI
- LI au - jour-d'hui O MA - LI de de - main Les champs fleu -

rall. 2nd time

No - tre dra - peau ___ se - ra li - ber - té.
-ris - sent d'es - pé - ran - ce, Les coeurs vi - brent de con -

rall. 2nd time

Pour l'A - frique et pour toi MA - LI

No-tre com-bat se-ra u-ni-té. O MA- fian - ce.

2. *Debout, villes et campagnes,*
   Debout, femmes, jeunes et vieux
   Pour la Patrie en marche
   Vers l'avenir radieux
   Pour notre dignité.
   Renforçons bien nos rangs,
   Pour le salut public
   Forgeons le bien commun
   Ensemble, au coude à coude
   Faisons le chantier du bonheur.

3. *La voie est dure, très dure*
   Qui mène au bonheur commun.
   Courage et dévouement, } (bis.)
   Vigilance à tout moment,
   Vérité des temps anciens,
   Vérité de tous les jours,
   Le bonheur par le labeur
   Fera le MALI de demain.

4. *L'Afrique se lève enfin*
   Saluons ce jour nouveau.
   Saluons la liberté,
   Marchons vers l'unité.
   Dignité retrouvée
   Soutient notre combat.
   Fidèles à notre serment
   De faire l'Afrique unie
   Ensemble, debout mes frères
   Tous au rendez-vous de l'honneur.

English Translation by
T. M. CARTLEDGE

1. At your call, MALI,
So that you may prosper,
Faithful to your destiny,
We shall all be united,
One people, one goal, one faith
For a united Africa.
If the enemy should show himself
Within or without,
On the ramparts
We are ready to stand and die.

Chorus   For Africa and for you, MALI,
Our banner shall be liberty.
For Africa and for you, MALI,
Our fight shall be for unity.
Oh, MALI of today,
Oh, MALI of tomorrow,
The fields are flowering with hope
And hearts are thrilling with confidence.

2. Stand up, towns and countryside,
Stand up, women, stand up young and old,
For the Fatherland on the road
Towards a radiant future.
For the sake of our dignity
Let us strengthen our ranks;
For the public well-being
Let us forge the common good.
Together, shoulder to shoulder,
Let us work for happiness.

3. The road is hard, very hard,
That leads to common happiness.
Courage and devotion,
Constant vigilance,
Courage and devotion,
Constant vigilance,
Truth from olden times,
The truths of every day,
Happiness through effort
Will build the MALI of tomorrow.

4. Africa is at last arising,
Let us greet this new day.
Let us greet freedom,
Let us march towards unity.
Refound dignity
Supports our struggle.
Faithful to our oath
To make a united Africa,
Together, arise, my brothers,
All to the place where honour calls.

MALTA

Innu Malti

HYMN OF MALTA

Words by
DUN KARM PSAILA (1871-1961)
Translated by
MAY BUTCHER

Music by
ROBERT SAMMUT M.D.
(1870-1934)

Maestoso

1. Guard her, O Lord, _____ as _____ ev - er Thou_ hast_ guard - ed _____ This Mo - ther
Lil din l-Art he - lwa, _____ l-Omm li _____ tat - na_ i - si - mha _____ Ha - res, Mu -
2. May he who rules _____ for _____ wis - dom be_ re - gard - ed, _____ In mas - ter
Agh - ti, Kbir Al - la, _____ id deh'n _____ lil min_ jah - ki - mha, _____ Rodd il - hnie -

Dun Karm Psaila, Malta's greatest poet, was asked to write these words for a school hymn to
Sammut's music. He conceived the idea of writing a hymn to Malta in the form of a prayer; he
wanted to unite all parties with the strong ties of religion and love of country.
It was first performed on 3rd February, 1923, and later declared to be the official anthem (On
7th April, 1941).

land_____ so dear whose name__ we__ bear!_____
-lej,_____ Kif dej - jem Int__ ha - rist:_____
mer - cy, strength in man__ in - crease!_____
-na_____ lis - sid, sah-ha__ 'l-had-di - em:

Keep her in mind____ whom Thou hast made so__ fair!_____
Fta - kar li lil - ha bil - oh - la dawl lib - bist!_____
Con - firm us all_____ in u - ni - ty__ and_ peace!_____
Sed - daq il - ghaq - da fil - Mal - tin u__ s - sliem!_____

MAURITANIA

Arr. by HENRY COLEMAN

D. $\mathsegment$ al Fine

MEXICO

Words by
FRANCISCO GONZÁLEZ BOCANEGRA
(1824-1861)
Translated by
Miss B. ROMERO
Versified by
J.E. HALES

Music by
JAIME NUNÓ
(1824-1908)

1. Me - xi - ca - nos al gri - to__ de gue - - rra El a -
1. Mex - i - cans, when the trum - pet__ is call - - ing, Grasp your

- ce - ro ap - res - tad y el bri - dón.__ Y re -
sword and your har - ness as - sem - ble. Let the

- tiem - ble en sus cen - tros la tie - rra, Al so -
guns with their thun - der ap - pal - ling Make the

Words chosen from a government competition.
First performed 16th September, 1854, at the National Theatre in Mexico.

-no - ro ru - gir del ca - ñón, Y re-
Earth's deep foun-da - tions to trem - ble. Let the

-tiem - ble en sus cen - tros la tie - - - rra al so-
guns with their thun - der ap - pal - - - ling Make the

-no - ro ru - gir del ca - ñón.
Earth's deep foun-da - tions to trem - ble.

Fine

ff

Fine

-sa reun ex-tra - ñoe - ne - mi - go Pro - fa-
e - ver the proud foe as-sail thee, And with

-nar___ con su plan - ta tu sue - lo Pien - sa ¡Oh
in - so-lent___ foot___ pro - fane thy ground, Know, dear

pa - tria que - ri - da! que el cie - lo Un sol-
Coun - try, thy sons shall not fail___ thee, Ev - 'ry

-da - do en ca - da hi - jo___ te dió Un___ sol-
one thy sol - dier shall be___ found, Thy sol - dier

-da-doen ca-da hi - jo te dió.
ev - 'ry___ one shall be found.

2. *¡Patria! ¡Patria! Tus hijos te juran*
Exhalar en tus aras su aliento,
Si el clarín, con su bélico acento,
Los convoca a lidiar con valor.
¡Para ti las guirnaldas de oliva!
¡Un recuerdo para ellos de gloria!
¡Un laurel para ti de victoria!
¡Un sepulcro para ellos de honor!

CORO: Mexicanos, etc.

2. Blessed Homeland, thy children have vowed them
If the bugle to battle should call,
They will fight with the last breath allowed them
Till on thy loved altars they fall.
Let the garland of olive thine be;
Unto them be deathless fame;
Let the laurel of victory be assigned thee,
Enough for them the tomb's honoured name.

CHORUS: Mexicans, etc.

MONACO

French words by
LOUIS CANIS

Music by
BELLANDO DE CASTRO
Arr. by HENRY COLEMAN

1. Prin - ci - pau - té Mo - na - co ma pa - tri - e, Oh! com-bien Dieu est pro - di - gue pour toi. Ciel tou-jours pur, ri - ves tou - jours fleu - ri - es, Ton Sou - ve - rain est plus ai - mé qu'un

Performed for the first time in 1867

Roi. Ton Sou-ve-rain est plus ai-mé qu'un Roi.

2. Fiers Compagnons de la Garde Civique,
Respectons tous la voix du Commandant.
Suivons toujours notre bannière antique.
Le tambour bat, marchons tous en Avant. *(bis)*

3. Oui, Monaco connut toujours des braves.
Nous sommes tous leurs dignes descendants.
En aucun temps nous ne fûmes esclaves,
Et loin de nous, régnèrent les tyrans. *(bis)*

4. Que le nom d'un Prince plein de clémence
Soit repété par mille et mille chants.
Nous mourons tous pour sa propre défense,
Mais après nous, combattrons nos enfants. *(bis)*

1. Principality of Monaco, my country,
Oh! how God is lavish with you.
An ever-clear sky, ever-blossoming shores,
Your Sovereign is better liked than a King. (repeat)

2. Proud Fellows of the Civic Guard,
Let us all listen to the Commander's voice.
Let us always follow our ancient flag.
Drums are beating, let us all march forward. (repeat)

3. Yes, Monaco always had brave men.
We all are their worthy descendants.
We never were slaves,
And far from us ruled the tyrants. (repeat)

4. Let the name of a Prince full of clemency
Be repeated in thousands and thousands of songs.
We shall all die in his defence,
But after us, our children will fight. (repeat)

MOROCCO

Hymne Cherifien

No words

This version conforms to the orchestration approved
by Si Mohammed Ben Youssef, Sultan of Morocco.
Arranged by LÉO MORGAN

MUSCAT AND OMAN

Transliteration of words by
RASHID BIN AZIZ, c.1922

YA RABBANA FAHFADH LANA

SULTANANA SA'ID

SA'ID BILTAYID

WAL 'IZZ AL-MAGID

WAHFADH LAHU ISTIQLALAHU

WA ADIM 'ALA AL-ISLAM

DHILLA LIWAIHI WAL MUSLIMIN.

Translation

God save our Sultan Said;
Happy may he be with our support,
Honour and glory.
His independence may be preserved,
His banners perpetual giving their shade
Over Islam and Muslims.

NEPAL

NATIONAL ANTHEM FOR
H.M. THE MAHARAJA DHIRAJA

Andante

Shri mân gum - bhi - ra ne - pâ - li pra-chan-da pra-tâ-pi bhu-pa-ti Shri pânch sar - kâr ma-hâ-râ-jâ - dhi-râ - ja ko sa-dâ ra-hos un - na-ti Ra -

-khun chi râ - yu ee - sha-le pra-jâ phai - li - yos pu-kâ - raun ja-ya pre-ma-le Hâ - mi ne - pâ - li bhâ - ee___ sâ - râ - le.

rall.

Free Translation

May glory crown you, courageous Sovereign, you,
the gallant Nepalese,
Shri Pansh Maharajadhiraja, our glorious ruler.
May he live for many years to come and may the
number of his subjects increase.
Let every Nepalese sing this with joy.

NETHERLANDS
Wilhelmus van Nassouwe

Words by
MARNIX van St. ALDEGONDE
(1540-1598)
(Official Netherlands Government translation)

Composer unknown

1. *Wil - hel - mus van Nas - sou - we Ben ick van*
1. Wil - liam of Nas - sau,— sci - on of Dutch and

Duit - schen bloet; Den Va - der - lant ghe -
an - cient line, I de - di - cate un -

- trou - we Blijf ick tot in den doet. Een
- dy - ing faith to this land of mine. A

Composer unknown: melody known from before 1572.
Song appeared in Valerius' "Gedenck-Clanck", 1626.
It has 15 verses in all.

prin - ce van O - ran - jen Ben ick
Prince am I, un - daunt - ed, of

vrij on - ver - veert; Den Co - ninck
O - range e'er free, To the King of

van His - pan - jen Heb ick al - tijd ghe - eert.
Spain I've gran - ted a life's loy - al - ty.

2. *Mijn schilt en de betrouwen*
   Sijt ghij, O Godt mijn Heer,
   Op u soo wil ick bouwen
   Verlaet mij nimmermeer!
   Dat ick doch vroom mach blijven
   U dienaer t'aller stondt,
   Die Tyranny verdrijven,
   Die mij mijn hert doorwondt.

2. My shield and my protection
   Art Thou my Lord and God.
   On Thee I build mine action,
   Be evermore my rod.
   That I be Thine eternal
   And serve Thee fair and true
   To chase tyrants infernal
   Who my heart undo.

NETHERLANDS ANTILLES
Curaçao

Words by
FRIAR RADULPHUS

Music by
FRIAR CANDIDUS

1. Den tur na-ci-ón nos pa-tri-a Ta po-co con-

-o - cí Den di la-mar in-men-so E

ta pa-ra scon-dí Ma toch nos ta sti-

Written when Curaçao was a colony of Holland, this is sung only on the islands.
It follows the Netherlands National Anthem. The words are in the Papiamento language.
An official National Anthem for the Netherlands Antilles is under consideration.

-me - le Ar - i - ba tur na - cíon. Su glor-

-i - a nos ta can - ta Di hen - ter nos cur - a - zón.

2. Nos tera ta baranca
    Y solo ta quima,
    Bandera di Hulanda
    Ta cubri nos lugá
    Un Reina poderosa
    Wilhelmina di Nassau
    Cu mano generosa
    Ta goberna CORSOW!

Free Translation

1. Among the nations our country
    Is little known
    For the immense sea
    Is there to hide it.
    Yet we love it
    Above all nations.
    We sing its glory
    With all our heart.

2. Our country is rugged
    And burnt by the sun.
    The flag of Holland
    Covers our land.
    A mighty Queen,
    Wilhelmina of Nassau,
    With a generous hand
    Governs Curaçao.

NEWFOUNDLAND

Words by
CHARLES CAVENDISH BOYLE
(1849-1916)

Music by
C. H. PARRY
(1848-1918)
Arr. by HENRY COLEMAN

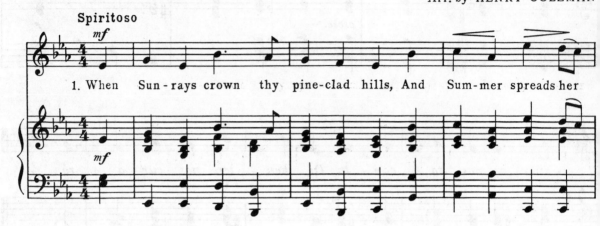

1. When Sun-rays crown thy pine-clad hills, And Sum-mer spreads her

hand, When sil-vern voi-ces tune thy rills We love thee smil-ing land,

love thee smil-ing land, We love thee, we

Sir Charles Cavendish Boyle wrote the words when he was
Governor of Newfoundland. It was first performed in pub-
lic 21st January 1902. Both this Anthem and that for Great
Britain are used.

love   thee, we love thee, smil - ing land.

2. When blinding storm-gusts fret thy shore,
  And wild waves lash thy strand,
  Thro' sprindrift swirl and tempest roar,
  We love thee, wind-swept land,
  We love thee, we love thee,
  We love thee, wind-swept land.

3. When spreads thy cloak of shimm'ring white,
  At Winter's stern command,
  Thro' shortened day and starlit night,
  We love thee, frozen land,
  We love thee, we love thee,
  We love thee, frozen land.

4. As loved our fathers, so we love,
  Where once they stood we stand,
  Their prayer we raise to heav'n above,
  God guard thee, Newfoundland,
  God guard thee, God guard thee,
  God guard thee, Newfoundland.

NEW ZEALAND
God Defend New Zealand

Words by
THOMAS BRACKEN (1843-1898)

Music by
JOHN J. WOODS (1849-193·
Arr. by VERNON GRIFFITH

HIGH VOICES I (*prominent*)

2. Men of ev-'ry creed and __ race Ga-ther here be-fore __ Thy __

HIGH VOICES II

2. Men of ev-'ry creed and race Ga-ther here be-fore Thy __

LOW VOICES

2. Men of ev-'ry creed and race Ga-ther here be-fore Thy

face, Ask-ing Thee to bless this place — God de-fend our Free-

face, Ask-ing Thee __ to __ bless this place — God de-fend our Free-

face, __ Ask-ing Thee to bless this place __ God de-fend our Free-

land. From dis - sen - sion, en - vy,— hate, And cor - rup - tion, guard our—

land. From dis - sen - sion, en - vy, hate,— And cor - rup - tion, guard our

land. From dis - sen - sion, en - vy, hate, And cor - rup - tion, guard our

State; Make our coun-try good and great— God de - fend New Zea - land.

State; Make our coun-try— good and great— God de - fend New Zea - land.

State; Make our coun-try good and— great— God de - fend New Zea - land.

D.C. for v.3

NICARAGUA

Words by
SALOMÓN IBARRA MAYORGA
English versification by
MARY ELIZABETH SHAW

Composer unknown
(Composed before 1821)

Maestoso

Sal - ve a ti Ni - ca - ra - gua en tu
Hail Ni - ca - ra - gua! the thun - der of

sue - lo,   ya no ru - ge la
can - non   Calls thy peo - ple no

voz del cañ - ón   ni se ti - ñe con san - gre de her -
lon - ger to war,   And thy ban - ner, twin co - loured flies

The words formerly sung were replaced by these
words in 1939 by a governmental decree.

By permission of J.B.Cramer & Co.Ltd.

-mo - sa la paz en tu cie - lo, na - da em - pa - ñe tu
peace spreads her wings o'er thy coun-try, Whose fair glo - ry its

glo - ria in-mor-tal que el tra - ba - jo es tu dig - no lau -
pure - ness re-tains; For thy lau - rels by la - bour are

-rel y el ho - nor es tu en-se-ña tri-un-fal,
won. Ho-nour, un - dimmed, thy shin-ing en - sign re - mains,

es tu en - se - ña tri - un - fal.
thy shin - ing en - sign re - mains.

NIGER
La Nigerienne

Words by MAURICE THIRIET

Music by
ROBERT JACQUET (b.1896)
NICK FRIONNET (b. 1911)

1. Au - près du grand Ni - ger puis-sant Qui rend la na-tu-re plus bel - le,

So - yons fiers et re - con - nais-sants De no-tre li-ber-té nou - vel - le.

E - vi-tons les vai - nes que-rel - les A-fin d'é-par - gner no-tre sang;

Allegro (2 in à bar)

- bout Ni-ger: De - bout!___ Que no - tre œu - vre fé - conde Ra-

-jeu - nis-se le cœur de ce vieux con - ti - nent___ Et

que ce chant s'en - tende___ aux qua - tre coins du mon - de Com-

- me le cri d'un Peuple é - qui-table et vail - lant!___ De -

S

-bout Ni-ger: De - bout!___ Sur le sol et sur l'on - de, Au

ryth - me des tam - tams, dans leur son gran - dis - sant, Res-

-tons u - nis, tou - jours,___ et que cha-cun ré-pon - de A ce noble a - ve-

-nir qui nous dit "En___ a - vant."

poco rall.

D. % Fine

2. *Nous retrouvons dans nos enfants*
 Toutes les vertus des Ancêtres:
 Pour lutter dans tous les instants
 Elles sont notre raison d'être.
 Nous affrontons le fauve traître
 A peine armés le plus souvent
 Voulant subsister dignement
 Sans detruire pour nous repaître.
 Dans la steppe où chacun ressent
 La soif, dans le Sahel brûlant,
 Marchons, sans défaillance, en maîtres
 Magnanimes et vigilants.

Translation by
T. M. CARTLEDGE

1. By the waters of the mighty Niger
 Which adds to the beauty of nature,
 Let us be proud and grateful
 For our new-won liberty.
 Let us avoid vain quarrelling
 So that our blood may be spared,
 And may the glorious voice
 Of our race, free from tutelage,
 Rise unitedly, surging as from one man,
 To the dazzling skies above
 Where its eternal soul, watching over us,
 Brings greatness to the country.

2. We find again in our children
 All the virtues of our ancestors.
 Such virtues are our inspiration
 For fighting at every moment.
 We confront ferocious and treacherous animals
 Often scarcely armed,
 Seeking to live in dignity,
 Not slaying with a lust to kill.
 In the steppe where all feel thirst,
 In the burning desert,
 Let us march tirelessly forward
 As magnanimous and vigilant masters.

Chorus

Arise, Niger, arise! May our fruitful work
Rejuvenate the heart of this old continent,
And may this song resound around the world
Like the cry of a just and valiant people.
Arise, Niger, arise! On land and river
To the rhythm of the swelling drum-beats' sound
May we ever be united and may each one of us
Answer the call of this noble future that says to us, "Forward!"

NIGERIA

Words by
LILIAN JEAN WILLIAMS

Music by
FRANCES BENDA

Moderato

1. Ni - ger - i - a we hail thee, Our own dear na - tive land, Though
2. Our flag shall be a sym - bol That truth and jus - tice reign, In
3. O God of all cre - a - tion, Grant this our one re - quest, Help

tribe and tongue may dif - fer, In bro - ther - hood we stand, Ni -
peace or bat - tle hon - our'd, And this we count as gain, To
us to build a na - tion Where no man is op - pressed, And

- ger - ians all, and proud to serve Our sove reign Mo - ther - land.
hand on to our child - ren A ban - ner with - out stain.
so with peace and plen - ty Ni - ger - ia may be blessed.

The words and music were chosen as the result of a competition. It became
the National Anthem on 1st October, 1960, when Nigeria became independent.
© Copyright 1960 by the Federal Government of Nigeria

NORWAY
Ja, vi elsker dette landet

Words by
BJÖRNSTERNE BJÖRNSSON
(1832-1910)

Translated by
G. M. GATHORNE-HARDY

Music by
RIKARD NORDRAAK
(1842-1866)

Moderato.

1. Ja, vi els - ker det - te lan - det,
1. Yes, we love with fond de - vo - tion

som det sti - ger frem, fu - ret, vær - bitt
This, the land that looms Rug - ged, storm-scarred,

o - ver van - net med de tu - sen hjem.
o'er the o - cean, With her thou - sand homes.

Adopted as the National Anthem in 1864, when first public recital
was given on the fiftieth anniversary of the Norwegian constitution.
Björnsson is one of Norway's great dramatists and poets.

Els - ker, els - ker det og ten - ker på vår far og
Love her, in our love re - call - ing Those who gave us

mor og den sa - ga - natt som sen - ker
birth, And old tales which night, in fall - ing,

dröm - me på vår jord, og den sa - ga - natt som
Brings as dreams to earth, And old tales which night, in

sen - ker, sen - ker dröm - me på vår jord!
fall - ing, Brings as dreams, as dreams to earth.

2. *Norske mann i hus og hytte,*
takk din store Gud!
Landet ville han beskytte,
skjönt det mörkt så ut.
Alt, hva fedrene har kjempet,
mödrene har grett,
har den Herre stille lempet,
så vi vant vår rett,
har den Herre stille lempet,
så vi vant, vi vant vår rett.

3. *Ja, vi elsker dette landet,*
som det stiger frem
furet, værbitt over vannet,
med de tusen hjem!
Og som fedres kamp har hevet
det av nöd til seir,
også vi, når det blir krevet,
for dets fred slår leir,
ogsa vi, nar det blir krevet,
for dets fred, dets fred slår leir!

2. Norseman, whatsoe'er thy station,
Thank thy God, whose power
Willed and wrought the land's salvation
In her darkest hour.
All our mothers sought with weeping
And our sires in fight,
God has fashioned, in his keeping, { *bis. (repeating "we gained"*
Till we gained our right.   { *the second time)*

3. Yes, we love with fond devotion
This our land that looms
Rugged, storm-scarred, o'er the ocean
With her thousand homes.
And, as warrior sires have made her
Wealth and fame increase,
At the call we too will aid her, { *bis. (repeating "to guard"*
Armed to guard her peace.   { *the second time)*

PAKISTAN

Words by
ABUL ASAR HAFEEZ JULLUNDURI

Music by
AHMAD G. CHAGLA
Arr. by BRYSON GERRARD

Music officially accepted as National Anthem of Pakistan, December 1953.
Words officially accepted as text of National Anthem of Pakistan, August 1954.

Tar - ju - ma - ni ma - zi - sha - ni hal ja - ni is - tik - bal

Say - yai, khu - dai zul ja - - lal.

Free Translation

1. Blessed be the sacred land,
   Happy be the beauteous realm,
   Symbol of high resolve,
   Land of Pakistan.
   Blessed be thou citadel of faith.

2. The Order of this Sacred Land
   Is the might of the brotherhood of the people.
   May the nation, the country, and the State
   Shine in glory everlasting.
   Blessed be the goal of our ambition

3. This flag of the Crescent and the Star
   Leads the way to progress and perfection,
   Interpreter of our past, glory of our present,
   Inspiration of our future,
   Symbol of Almighty's protection.

PANAMA

Words by
JERÓNIMO de la OSSA
(1847-1907)
English versification by
SEBASTIAN SHAW

Music by
SANTOS JORGE A.
(1870-1941)
Arr. by **MARTIN SHAW**

CHORUS

1. Al - can - za - mos por fin la vic -
1. Fi - nal vic - to - ry honoured then our

- to - ria, en el cam - po fe - liz de la u - nión, Con ar -
sto - ry, When at last we gained u - nion's fair field. Shin - ing

- dien - tes ful - go - res de glo - ria se ilu -
bright in the blaze of her glo - ry, Now be -

This anthem was used for the first time on 4th November, 1903,
when the Panamanian people carried the flag of the new Republic
of Panama through the streets of the capital.
Words copyright J.B.Cramer & Co.Ltd.

-mi - na la nue - va Na - ción___ Con ar-dien-tes ful-go - res de
-hold, the new nation is re - vealed!___ Shin-ing bright in the blaze of her

Fine

glo - ria se ilu - mi - na la nue - va Na - ción.
glo - ry, Now be-hold, the new nation is re - vealed!

Fine

VERSE
p dolce

Es pre-ci - so cu-brir con un ve - lo, del pa -
We re-joice that, the Cal - va - ry end - ed, And the

-sa - do el cal-va - rio y la cruz,___ y que a -
Cross be - ing veiled in the past,___ Gen - tle

-gir á tus pies am-bos ma - - res, que dan
feet roar two o - ceans, which se - - ver, For your

rum - bo a tu no - ble mi - sión.
mis - sion, a - way for all time.

D.S. %

2. *En tu suelo cubierto de flores,*
   A los besos del tibio terral,
   Terminaron guerreros fragores,
   Sólo reina el amor fraternal.
   Adelante la pica y la pala,
   Al trabajo sin más dilación:
   Y seremos asi prez y gala
   De este mundo feraz de Colón.

2. From your soil, where gay flowers are greeted
   By the warmth of the breezes' caress,
   Far the clamours of war have retreated;
   Love fraternal your future will bless.
   Then with spade and with hammer, untiring,
   To his task let each man set his hand;
   So, to honour and glory aspiring,
   Shall we prosper Columbus' fair land.

PARAGUAY

Words by
FRANCISCO ACUÑA de FIGUEROA (1790-1862)
Versified English version by
T. M. CARTLEDGE

Music by
FRANCISCO ACUÑA de FIGUEROA
Arr. by REMBERTO GIMENEZ (b. 1899)

Adopted as National Anthem, 1846
This present arrangement was declared the official version in May 1934.
Francisco Acuña de Figueroa also wrote the words of the Uruguayan Anthem

-do, Basta!..., di - jo y el ce - tro rom -
-ing, 'Tis e - nough! they cried and broke the pow-ers that had

-pió. Nue - stros pa - dres li -
reigned. Our fore - fa - thers, mag -

-dian - do gran - dio - - - sos, I lus -
-ni - fi - cent - ly fight - - - ing, Showed their

-tra - ron su glo - ria mar - cial; Y tro -
mar - tial___ glo - ry and pow'r; And when

-so - res, ni sier - vos, a - lien - tan, Don - de
ty - rants nor slaves can con - tin - ue Where there

re - i - nan u - nión, é i - gual - dad, u - nión, é i - gual-
reign e - qual - i - ty and u - ni - ty, where reign e - qual - i -

-dad, u - nión, é i - gual - dad. _____
-ty, and where reign u - ni - ty. _____

ff

PERU

Words by
JOSÉ DE LA TORRE UGARTE
(1798-1878)

Music by
JOSÉ BERNARDO ALCEDO (1798-1878)
Arr. by HENRY COLEMAN

Somos li - bres, se - á - mos lo

siem - pre, se - á - mos - lo siem - pre, y-an - tes nie - gue sus

lu - ces sus lu - ces sus lu - ces el sol, que fal-

Words and music chosen as result of a competition for a national anthem
promoted by General San Martin in 1821. Text (revised) declared
unalterable by a law which came into force 31st December, 1912.

- te - mos al vo - to so - lem - ne que la Pa - tria al E - ter-no e-le -

-vó____ que fal - te - mos al vo - to so - lem - ne que__ la

Pa - tria al E - ter - no e-le - vó____ que fal - te - mos al vo - to so -

-lem - ne que__ la Pa - tria al E - ter - no-e-le - vó.____

Fine

VERSE

1. Lar - go tiem - po_el pe - rua - no_o-pri - mi - do la_o-mi-

-no - sa ca-de - na_arras-tró;_____ con-de - na-do_a_u-na cruel ser-vi-

-dum - - bre, lar-go tiem-po lar-go tiem-po lar - go

tiem-po_en si-len - cio gi-mió.____ Mas a-pe-nas el gri-to sa-

-gra-do   ¡Li-ber-tad! en sus cos - tas___ se o - yó,   la in-do-

-len - cia de es-cla - vo sa-cu - - de, la hu-mi - lla-do   la hu-mi-

-lla-do   la hu-mi - lla - do cerviz le - van - tó,_____ la hu-mi-

-lla - do cer-viz le-van - tó   cer-viz le-van-tó.___   So - mos

Free Translation

CHORUS

We are free; let us always be so,
and let the sun rather deny its light
than that we should fail the solemn vow
which our Country raised to God.

VERSE

For a long time the Peruvian, oppressed,
dragged the ominous chain;
condemned to cruel serfdom,
for a long time he moaned in silence.
But as soon as the sacred cry of
Freedom! was heard on his coasts
he shakes the indolence of the slave,
he raises his humiliated head.

NOTE: There were originally six verses, but
this first verse only is now sung.

THE PHILIPPINES

Words by
JOSÉ PALMA (1876-1903)
Translated by
Hon. CAMILO OSIAS and M.A.L. LANE

Music by
JULIAN FELIPE (1861-1944)

First performed in conjunction with the reading of the Act of
Proclamation of Philippine Independence, 12 June 1898.
The words were written in 1899.

Di ma-lu-lu-pig Mag-pa kay-lan pa man
Ne'er shall in-va-ders Tram-ple thy sa-cred shore.

Sa___ i-yong ha ngi't bun-dok Sa da-gat
Ev-er with-in thy skies and through thy clouds And

mo't ka-la-ngi-tan Ay may mit-hing tu-mi-ti-
o'er thy hills and sea Do we be-hold the ra-diance,

-bók Ang la-ya mong___ mi-na-ma-
Feel the throb, Of glo-rious lib-er-

pi - ling mo'y kay gan - dá_____ At kung sa
- brace 'tis rap - ture to lie;_____ But it is

ka - ling sa iyo'y may i - big pu - mas - lang La-ngit sa
glo - ry ev - er, When thou__ art__ wronged For us, thy

a - min ang ma - ma - tay._____
sons, to suf - fer and die._____

D.C.al Fine

POLAND

Translated by
MARTIN SHAW

Words and Music by
General JÓSEF WYBICKI
(1747-1822)

1. Jeszc-ze Pol-ska nie zgi-ne-ta,___ kie-dy my zy-
1. Po-land still is ours for ev-er,___ Long as Poles re-

-je-my, co nam ob-ca prze-moc wzie-ta,___
-main;___ Chains the foe bound on her nev-er___

szab-la od-bie-rze-my. Marsz, marsz, Da-brow-ski;
Shall the foe re-tain.___ On! On! Da-bru-ski!★ from

This song, first sung in 1795, was a favourite with the Polish
Legions in the Napoleonic wars. It has been sung all over
Poland since 1912; in 1927 it was authorized as its National
Anthem by the new Polish republican government.
★General Dabruski (1755-1818) commanded the Polish Legions.

2. *Przejdziem Wisłę, przejdziem Wartę,*
   będziem Polakami,
   dał nam przykład Bonaparte
   jak zwyciężać mamy.
       Marsz, marsz, Dąbrowski

2. Vistula and Wartar over,
   Poles we'll ever be;
   And from Bonaparte discover
   Paths to victory.
       On! On! etc.

3. *Jak Czarniecki do Poznania*
   po szwedzkim zaborze,
   dla ojczyzny ratowania
   wrócim się przez morze.
       Marsz, marsz, Dąbrowski

3. When the Swede had forged our chain,
   The Fatherland to save,
   Czarniecki, Poznan town to gain,
   Plunged into the wave.
       On! On! etc.

PORTUGAL

Words by
HENRIQUE LOPES DE MENDONÇA (1856-1931)

Music by
ALFREDO KEIL
(1850-1907)
Arr. by HENRY COLEMAN

First played January 1890, approved as the National Anthem in 1910.

Pá - tria, sen - te - se a voz___ Dos teus e - gré - gios a-

vós, Que há - de gui-ar - te à vi - tó - ri-a! Às

ar - mas! Às ar - mas! So-bre a ter - ra, so - bre o

CHORUS

mar___ Às ar - mas! Às ar - mas! Pe - la

Pá - tria lu - tar!___ Con-tra os ca-nhões mar-char, mar-char!

2. Desfralda a invicta bandeira
   Á luz viva do teu céu!
   Brade á Europa á terra inteira:
   Portugal não pereceu!
   Beija o solo teu jucundo
   O Oceano a rugir d'amor;
   E o teu braço vencedor
   Deu novos mundos ao mundo!

   Ás armas, ás armas!
   Sobre a terra, sobre o mar,
   Ás armas, ás armas!
   Pela pátria lutar!
   Contra os canhões marchar,
   Marchar!

3. Saudai o sol que desponta
   Sobre um ridente porvir;
   Seja o eco de uma afronta
   O sinal do ressurgir.
   Ráios dessa aurora forte
   São como beijos de mãe
   Que nos guardam, nos sustêm
   Contra as injúrias da sorte.

   Ás armas, ás armas!
   Sobre a terra, sobre o mar,
   Ás armas, ás armas!
   Pela pátria lutar!
   Contra os canhões marchar,
   Marchar!

U

Official English Paraphrase

1.   Heroes of the sea, noble race
valiant and immortal nation,
now is the hour to raise up on high once more
Portugal's splendour.
From out of the mists of memory,
oh Homeland, we hear the voices
of your great forefathers
that shall lead you on to victory!

CHORUS

To arms, to arms
on land and sea!
To arms, to arms
to fight for our Homeland!
To march against the enemy guns!

2.   Unfurl the unconquerable flag
in the bright light of your sky!
Cry out to all Europe and the whole world
that Portugal has not perished.
Your happy land is kissed
by the Ocean that murmurs with love.
And your conquering arm
has given new worlds to the world!

CHORUS

To arms, to arms
on land and sea!
To arms, to arms
to fight for our Homeland!
To march against the enemy guns!

3.   Salute the Sun that rises
on a smiling future:
let the echo of an insult be
the signal for our revival.
The rays of that powerful dawn
are like a mother's kisses
that protect us and support us
against the insults of fate.

CHORUS

To arms, to arms
on land and sea!
To arms, to arms
to fight for our Homeland!
To march against the enemy guns!

RUMANIA
Trăiască Regele

Words by
VASILE ALECSANDRI

Music by
EDWARD A. HÜBSCH (1813-1894)
Arr. by HENRY COLEMAN

Tră - ias - că Re - ge - le În
pa - ce şi o - nor, De ţa - ră iu - bi -
- tor Şi-a - pă - ră - tor de ţa - ră!

This National Anthem of Rumania (which was proclaimed a
kingdom on 10th May, 1881) is at present not sung inside
Rumania as the anthem which follows has officially replaced it.

Fi - e Domn glo - ri - os _____ Pes - te -

- noi, Fi - e'n veci no - ro -

- cos _____ În _____ răz - boi!

O! Doam - ne _____ Sfin - te, Ce - resc Pă -

-rin - te, Sus - ti - ne cu - a ta

mâ - nă Co - roa - na Ro - mâ - nă! -nă!

2. *Trăiască Patria*
Cât soarele ceresc,
Rai dulce, românesc,
Ce poartă-un mare nume!
Fie'n veci el ferit
De nevoi!
Fie'n veci locuit
De eroi!
O! Doamne Sfinte,
Ceresc Părinte
Întinde-a ta mână
Pe ţara română!

1. Long live our King
    In peace and honour,
    Loving his country
    Defending our fatherland!
    Let him be glorious
    Rule over us,
    Always victorious
    In war.
    O Lord the Holy,
    Our heavenly Father,
    Support with thy hands
    The Rumanian Crown!

2. Long live our fatherland
    As long as the sun,
    Sweet paradise
    With glorious name!
    Let it always be free
    Of worries!
    Let it always be inhabited
    By heroes!
    O Lord the Holy
    Our heavenly Father,
    Protect with thy hand
    The Rumanian land!

Pronunciation:

ă like er in "father"
Î like u in "une" in French
e (throughout) as in "get"
ţ as ts

ce as che
Şi-a as sha
veci as vech
ge as in gentle

RUMANIA

Words by
EUGEN FRUNZA and DAN DESLIU

Music by
MATEI SOCOR

1. Te slă - vim, Ro - mâ - ni - e, pă -
2. (In - fră) - țit fi - va veș - nic al
3. (Noi u) - zi - ne clă - dim, ro - dul

-mânt pă - rin-tesc, Mân - dre pla - iuri sub ce - rul tău
nos - tru po - por Cu po - po - rul so - vi - e - tic e -
hol - dei spo-rim, Vrem în pa - ce cu ori - ce po -

paș - nic ro-desc. E zdro - bit al tre - cu - tu - lui
-li - be - ra - tor. Le - ni - nis - mul ni-e far, și tă -
-por să tră - im. Dar duș - ma - nii de-ar fi să ne

This officially became the National Anthem in 1953

jug bles - te - mat, Nu za - dar - nic stră - bu - nii e -
-ri - e si-a-vânt, Noi ur - măm cu cre - din - ță Par -
cal - ce în prag, Îi vom frân - ge în nu - me - le-a

-roi au lup - tat, As - tăzi noi____ îm - pli - nim vi - sul
-ti - dul ne'n-frânt, Fa - u - rim____ so - cia - lis - mul pe-al
tot ce ni-e drag. Î nāl - ța____ vom spre glo - rie al

CHORUS

lor mi - nu - nat.
tā - rii pā-mânt. Pu - ter - ni - cā, li - be - rā,____ Pe
Pa - tri-ei steag.

1. We glorify thee, Rumania, soil of our parents,
    Fine orchards are bearing fruit under thy peaceful sky,
    The accursed yoke of the past is smashed,
    Not in vain have fought our ancestral heroes,
    Nowadays we are carrying out their wonderful dream.

        Chorus: Strong, free,
                    Mistress of thy fate
                    Long live the Rumanian
                    Popular Republic!

2. May our nation be always fraternal
    With the Soviet people, our liberators.
    Leninism is our guiding light, our strength and our enthusiasm,
    We follow with faith the unvanquished party,
    We are creating socialism on our Country's soil.

3. We are building new factories, we are increasing the yield of the harvest,
    We want to live in peace with any nation,
    But should the foes cross our threshold,
    We shall break them in the name of all that is dear to us
    And shall raise towards glory the flag of our Fatherland

SAN MARINO

Words by
GIOSUÈ CARDUCCI

Music by
FEDERICO CONSOLO
(1841-1906)

Largo solemno

O - no - re a te o - no - re o an - ti - ca Re - pu - bli - ca vir - tuo - - - sa - tuo - - - sa - ge - ne - ro - - sa fi - den - te o - no - re a

Free Translation

Honour to you, O ancient Republic,
Virtuous, generous, faithful!
Honour to you, and live eternally
Within the life and the glory of Italy.

SAUDI ARABIA

Music by
A.R. AL-HATIB

No words

First performed 1947, adopted 1950.

SENEGAL

Words by
LEOPOLD SÉDAR SENGHOR (b.1906)

Music by
HERBERT PEPPER

KORA Cadenza   **Alla Marcia**

1. Pin - cez tous vos Ko - ras, Frap-pez les ba - la - fons, Le

Lion rouge a ru - gi Le Domp - teur de la brousse d'un

bond s'est é - lan - cé Dis - si - pant les tén - è - bres. So -

Senegal became independent on 4th April 1960
This National Anthem was adopted in 1960
The words are by the President, Leopold Sédar Senghor

*Harp-Lute of the Senegalese Griots.

2. *Sénégal, toi le fils de l'écume du Lion,*
   Toi surgi de la nuit au galop des chevaux,
   Rends-nous, oh! rends-nous l'honneur de nos Ancêtres,
   Splendides comme ébène et forts comme le muscle
   Nous disons droits– l'épée n'a pas une bavure.

3. *Sénégal, nous faisons nôtre ton grand dessein:*
   Rassembler les poussins à l'abri des milans
   Pour en faire, de l'Est à l'Ouest, du Nord au Sud,
   Dressé, un même peuple, un peuple sans couture
   Mais un peuple tourné vers tous les vents du monde.

4. *Sénégal, comme toi, comme tous nos héros,*
   Nous serons durs sans haine et des deux bras ouverts.
   L'épée, nous la mettrons dans la paix du fourreau,
   Car le travail sera notre arme et la parole.
   Le Bantou est un frère, et l'Arabe et le Blanc.

5. *Mais que si l'ennemi incendie nos frontières*
   Nous serons tous dressés et les armes au poing:
   Un Peuple dans sa foi défiant tous les malheurs,
   Les jeunes et les vieux, les hommes et les femmes.
   La Mort, oui! Nous disons la Mort, mais pas la honte.

Free Translation by
ELIZABETH P. COLEMAN

1. Sound, all of you, your Koras ✴
   Beat the drums,
   The red Lion has roared,
   The Tamer of the bush with one leap has rushed forward
   Scattering the gloom.
   > Light on our terrors,
   > Light on our hopes.
   Arise, brothers, Africa behold united.

Chorus

Shoulder to shoulder,
O people of Senegal, more than brothers to me, arise!
Unite the sea and the springs,
Unite the steppe and the forest.
Hail, mother Africa,
Hail, mother Africa.

2. Senegal, thou son of the Lion,
   Arise in the night with great speed,
   Restore, oh, restore to us the honour of our ancestors,
   Magnificent as ebony and strong as muscles,
   We are a straight people—the sword has no fault.

3. Senegal, we make your great design our own:
   To gather the chicks, sheltering them from kites,
   To make from them, from East to West, from North to South,
   A people rising as one, in seamless unity,
   Yet a people facing all the winds of the earth.

4. Senegal, like thee, like all our heroes,
   We will be stern without hatred, and with open arms.
   The sword we will put peacefully in its sheath,
   For work and words will be our weapon.
   The Bantu is our brother, the Arab, and the White man too.

5. But if the enemy violates our frontiers,
   We will all be ready, weapons in our hands;
   A people in its faith defying all evil;
   Young and old, men and women,
   Death, yes! but not dishonour.

SIERRA LEONE

Words by
C. N. FYLE

Music by JOHN J. AKAR
Arr. by HENRY COLEMAN

Maestoso

1. High we ex-alt__ thee, realm of the free; Great is the love__ we
have for__ thee; Firm-ly u-nit-ed e-ver we stand,
Sing-ing thy praise, O__ nat-ive__land. We raise up our hearts and our

Written and composed in 1961 and adopted as the National Anthem
when Sierra Leone achieved independence on 27th April 1961
Both author and composer are Sierra Leonians; C.N. Fyle being a tutor at a
boys' high school, and John J. Akar Director of the Sierre Leone Broadcasting Service.

x

cresc.

voic - es on high, the hills and the val - leys re - e - cho our cry;

Bless-ing and peace be e - ver thine own, Land that we love, our— Sier - ra Le-one.

2. One with a faith that wisdom inspires,
   One with a zeal that never tires;
   Ever we seek to honour thy name,
   Ours is the labour, thine the fame.
   We pray that no harm on thy children may fall,
   That blessing and peace may descend on us all;
   So may we serve thee ever alone,
   Land that we love, our Sierra Leone.

3. Knowledge and truth our forefathers spread,
   Mighty the nations whom they led;
   Mighty they made thee, so too may we
   Show forth the good that is ever in thee.
   We pledge our devotion, our strength and our might,
   Thy cause to defend and to stand for thy right;
   All that we have be ever thine own,
   Land that we love, our Sierra Leone.

SINGAPORE
Majulah Singapura

Words and Music by
ZUBIR SAID
Arr. by HENRY COLEMAN

Ma-ri ki-ta ra'-yat Si-nga-pu-ra sa-ma sa-ma mĕ-nu-ju ba-ha-gi-a. Chi-ta chi-ta ki-ta yang mu-li-a Ber-ja-ya Si-nga-pu-ra!

For Royal Salute play from ★ to ★

First performed September, 1958. It became very popular and when
Singapore became self-governing on 3rd June 1959 it was decided to
make it the National Anthem. It was officially adopted as such
by the Legislative Assembly of Singapore on 30th November, 1959.

316

Free Translation

Let us, the people of Singapore, together march
forward towards happiness. Our noble aspiration
is to see Singapore achieve success.
Let us unite in a new spirit. We all pray:
"May Singapore Progress", "May Singapore Progress".

SOMALIA

Music, traditional.
Transcribed by R.A.Y. MITCHELL
Piano arr. by HENRY COLEMAN

This traditional music was adopted as the National Anthem when Somaliland became independent on 26 June, 1960. It was recorded by village musicians and transcribed by R.A.Y. Mitchell, Bandmaster of the Military Band of The Royal Highland Fusiliers, who performed it at Independence Celebrations.

UNION OF SOUTH AFRICA
Die Stem van Suid-Afrika
THE CALL OF SOUTH AFRICA

Words by
C.J. LANGENHOVEN, 1918
Official English translation, 1952, amended 1959

Music by
M.L. de VILLIERS, 1921

1. *Uit die blou van on se he - mel, uit die diep - te van ons*
2. *In die merg van ons ge - been - te, in ons hart en siel en*
1. Ring-ing out from our blue hea - vens, from our deep seas break-ing
2. In our bo - dy and our spi - rit, in our in - most heart held

see,   *Oor ons e - wi - ge ge - berg - tes waar die*
gees,   *In ons roem op ons ver - le - de, in ons*
round;   O - ver e - ver - last - ing moun - tains where the
fast;   In the prom - ise of our fu - ture and the

with emphasis

kran - se___ ant - woord gee, Deur ons vér ver - la - te
hoop op___ wat sal wees, In ons wil en werk en
e - choing crags re - sound; From our plains where creak - ing
glo - ry___ of our past; In our will, our work, our

vlak - tes met die kreun van os - se - wa___ Ruis die
wan - del, van ons wieg tot aan ons graf___ Deel geen
wag - ons cut their trails in - to the earth___ Calls the
striv - ing, from the cra - dle to the grave___ There's no

a tempo

stem van ons ge - lief - de, van ons land Suid - A - fri -
an - der land ons lief - de, trek geen an - der trou ons
spi - rit of our Coun - try, of the land that___ gave us
land that shares our lov - ing, and no bond that___ can en -

3 *In die songloed van ons somer, in ons winternag se kou,*
In die lente van ons liefde, in die lanfer van ons rou,
By die klink van huw'liks-klokkies, by die kluitklap op die kis—
Streel jou stem ons nooit verniet nie, weet jy waar jou kinders is.
Op jou roep sê ons nooit nee nie, sê ons altyd, altyd ja:
Om te lewe, on te sterwe-ja, ons kom, Suid-Afrika.

4 *Op U Almag vas vertrouend het ons vadere gebou:*
Skenk ook ons die krag, o Here! om te handhaaf en te hou—
Dat die erwe van ons vaad're vir ons kinders erwe bly:
Knegte van die Allerhoogste, teen die hele wêreld vry.
Soos ons vadere vertrou het, leer ook ons vertrou, o Heer—
Met ons land en met ons nasie sal dit wel wees, God regeer.

3 In the golden warmth of summer, in the chill of winter's air,
In the surging life of springtime, in the autumn of despair;
When the wedding bells are chiming or when those we love depart,
Thou dost know us for thy children and dost take us to thy heart.
Loudly peals the answering chorus: We are thine, and we shall stand,
Be it life or death, to answer to thy call, beloved land.

4 In thy power, Almighty, trusting, did our fathers build of old;
Strengthen then, O Lord, their children to defend, to love, to hold —
That the heritage they gave us for our children yet may be:
Bondsmen only to the Highest and before the whole world free.
As our fathers trusted humbly, teach us, Lord, to trust Thee still:
Guard our land and guide our people in Thy way to do Thy will.

SPAIN

18th Century tune
Orchestrated by
BARTOLOMÉ PÉREZ CASAS (b.1873)
Arr. by **MARTIN SHAW**

This anthem, the *Marcha Real,* dates from 3rd September, 1770, when it was declared by Royal Decree of Carlos III as the Spanish Royal March. In July 1942 General Franco issued a decree declaring it as the national hymn. There are no official words, though various writers have written verses at different times.

SUDAN

Words by
AHMED MOHAMED SALIH
English versification by
T. M. CARTLEDGE

Music by
Captain MURGAN
Arr. by T. M. CARTLEDGE

NAḤ-NU DJUN-DUL:-LÂH   DJUN-DUL-WA-TAN.
We are the ar - my of God   and   of   our land,

IN___ DÄ 'Â DÂ 'IL FI - DÂ   LÄM NA-KhUN.
We   shall ne - ver fail,   called   to   make   sac - ri - fice.

NÄ-TÄ-HAD-DAL MAUT   'END - ÄL - MI-ḤAN.
Wheth-er brav - ing death,   hard - ship   or pain,

YÄ BE-NIS - SÚ- DÃN, HÄ - ThÄ RAM - ZU- KUM:

Sons of the Su - dan, sum - moned now to serve.

YAḤ MI - LUL - 'EB, WÄ YAḤ- MÎ AR - DA- KUM.

Shoul - der - ing the task our coun - try to pre - serve.

Key to phonetic transliteration of Arabic text

⌃ for long vowels

Û as *oo* in *pool*

U nearer *u* in *put*

Ä as *a* in *cat*

A as *a* in *rather*

ÄYN approx. as *ine* in *fine*

Th ① as *th* in *thing*

Th ② as *th* in *this*

Ḥ aspirated at back of mouth

Kh like hard *ch* in German *Buch*

Gh like gutteral *r* in French *rang*

' like last *a* of *China*

AUT like *out*

SURINAM

Het Surinaamse Volkslied

Words by
C. A. HOEKSTRA (1893)

Music by
C. de PUY (1876)
Arr. by HENRY COLEMAN

Su - ri - na - me's trot - se stro - men, Su - ri -
God zij met ons Su - ri - na - me! Hij ver -

- na - me's heer - lijk land, Su - ri - na - me's fie - re
- heff' ons heer - lijk land! Doch dat elk zich dan ook

bo - men, Trouw zijn wij aan u ver - pand. Moch-ten weer de vlo - ten
scha - me, Die zijn e - re maakt ten schand. Recht en waar-heid te be -

Surinam uses the Netherlands National Anthem, and
the above National Anthem is played after that.

va - ren, Dat de han - del we - lig bloei, Dat fa-
-tracht - ten, Zeed'-lijk rein en vroom en vrij, Al wat

- brie - ken wel-vaart ba - ren, Dat hier al - les we - lig— groei!
slecht is te ver - ach - ten, Dat geeft aan ons land waar - dij!

Free Translation

Proud streams of Surinam,
Beautiful land of Surinam,
Stately trees of Surinam,
In faith we are pledged to you.
May the fleets sail again,
And the trade flourish,
May the factories bring prosperity
And may everything thrive!

God will be with our Surinam!
May He glorify our beautiful land!
But he who makes of his honour a disgrace,
Must then be filled with shame.
Try to be upright and truthful,
Morally pure, devout and joyful,
And despise everything which is bad;
This will make our country a worthy land!

SWEDEN

DU GAMLA, DU FRIA

Words by
RICHARD DYBECK
(1811-1877)

Folk melody
Arr. EDVIN KALLSTENIUS
(b. 1881-)

Maestoso

1. *Du gam - la, du fri - a, du fjäll - hö - ga Nord, du*
1. Thou an - cient, thou glo - rious, thou alp - crown - ed North, Where

tys - ta, du gläd - je - ri - ka skö - na! Jag
free - born and hap - py hearts are beat - ing! We

häl - sar dig, vä - nas - te land___ up - på jord, Din
hail thee, thou fair - est of lands___ on the earth. Thy

sol, din him-mel, di-na äng-der grö - na, din
sun, thy skies, thy flow-'ry val-leys greet - ing. Thy

sol din him-mel, di-na äng-der grö - na.
sun, thy skies, thy flow-'ry val-leys greet - ing.

2. *Du tronar på minnen från fornstora dar,*
   Då ärat ditt namn flög över jorden.
   Jag vet, att du är och du blir vad du var,
   :|: *Ack, jag vill leva, jag vill dö i Norden!* :|:

2. How proudly we dwell on thy great deeds of yore,
   What time thy name was famed in story;
   Thy sons still are valiant and brave as before:
   :|: In thee I'll live and die, thou land of glory! :|:

SWITZERLAND
Swiss Psalm

Schweizerpsalm
Words by L. WIDMER (1808-1868)
Cantique Suisse
CH. CHATELANET

Salmo Svizzero
Psalm Svizzer
J. A. BÜHLER

Music by
A. ZWYSSIG
(1808 - 1854)
Harm. G. DORET

Ger. 1. *Trittst im Mor - gen - rot da - her,___ seh ich dich im*
Fr. 1. *Sur nos monts, quand le so - leil___ An - nonce un bril -*
It. 1. *Quan - do bion - da au - ro - ra___ Il mat - tin c'in -*
Rom. 1. *In l'au - ro - ra la da - man___ at cu - gnuo - scha*
Eng. 1. When the morn - ing skies grow red___ And o'er us their

Strah - len - meer,___ dich, du Hoch - er - ha - be - ner,
-lant ré - veil,___ Et pré - dit d'un plus beau jour
-do - ra___ L'al - ma mia t'a - do - ra,
bain l'u - man___ spiert e - tern do - mi - na - tur,
ra - diance shed,___ Thou, O Lord, ap - pear - eth

The music was composed by Father Alberik Zwyssig, a monk, who adapted it to Leonhard Widmer's words in 1841
This was declared the official National Anthem by the Federal Government in September 1961
for a trial period of three years, ending on 31st December 1964.

GERMAN

2. *Kommst im Abendglühn daher,*
   Find ich dich im Sternenheer,
   Dich, du Menschenfreundlicher, Liebender!
   In des Himmels lichten Räumen
   Kann ich froh und selig träumen;
   Denn die fromme Seele ahnt
   Gott im hehren Vaterland.

3. *Ziehst im Nebelflor daher,*
   Such ich dich im Wolkenmeer,
   Dich, du Unergründlicher, Ewiger!
   Aus dem grauen Luftgebilde
   Bricht die Sonne klar und milde,
   Und die fromme Seele ahnt
   Gott im hehren Vaterland.

4. *Fährst im wilden Sturm daher,*
   Bist du selbst uns Hort und Wehr,
   Du, allmächtig Waltender, Rettender!
   In Gewitternacht und Grauen
   Lasst uns kindlich ihm vertrauen!
   Ja, die fromme Seele ahnt
   Gott im hehren Vaterland.

FRENCH

2. *Lorsqu'un doux rayon du soir*
   Joue encor dans le bois noir,
   Le cœur se sent plus heureux, près de Dieu.
   Loin des vains bruits de la plaine,
   L'âme en paix est plus sereine;
   Au ciel montent plus joyeux
   Les accents (émus) d'un cœur pieux.

3. *Lorsque dans la sombre nuit*
   La foudre éclate avec bruit,
   Notre cœur pressent encor le Dieu fort;
   Dans l'orage et la détresse,
   Il est notre forteresse.
   Offrons-lui des cœurs pieux
   Dieu nous bénira (du haut) des cieux.

4. *Des grands monts vient le secours,*
   Suisse, espère en Dieu toujours!
   Garde la foi des Aïeux, vis comme eux!
   Sur l'autel de la patrie
   Mets tes biens, ton cœur, ta vie!
   C'est le trésor précieux
   Que Dieu bénira (du haut) des cieux.

ITALIAN

2. *Se di nubi un velo*
   M'asconde il tuo cielo
   Pel tuo raggio anelo, Dio d'amor!
   Fuga o sole quei vapori,
   E mi rendi i tuoi favori,
   Di mia patria, deh pietà!
   Brilla, Sol di verità!

ROMANSCH

2. *Eir la saira in splendur*
   da las stailas i'l azur
   tai chattain nus creatur, tuotpussant!
   Cur cha'l firmamaint s'sclerescha
   in nos cour fidanza crescha
   Tia orma sainta ferm
   Dieu in tschêl, il Bap etern.

3. *Tü a nus nun est zoppà*
   cur il tschêl in nüvlas sta,
   Tü imperscrutabel spiert, tuotpussant!
   Tschêl e terra T'obedeschan,
   vent e nüvlas secundeschan.
   Tia orma sainta ferm
   Dieu in tschêl, il Bap etern.

4. *Eir l'orcan plü furius*
   nun At muossa main a nus
   sco il dirigent dal muond, tuotpussant!
   Eir in temporals terribels
   sun Teis uordens bain visibels.
   Tia orma sainta ferm
   Dieu in tschêl, il Bap etern.

English Translation

2. In the sunset Thou art nigh
   And beyond the starry sky,
   Thou, O loving Father, ever near.
   When to Heav'n we are departing,
   Joy and bliss Thou'lt be imparting
   For we feel and understand
   That Thou dwellest in this land.

3. When dark clouds enshroud the hills
   And grey mist the valley fills
   Yet, Thou art not hidden from Thy sons.
   Pierce the gloom in which we cower
   With Thy sunshine's cleansing power,
   Then we'll feel and understand
   That God dwelleth in this land.

4. Through the wild and stormy night,
   Thou doest shield us with Thy might,
   Omnipotent Saviour, Lord of all,
   Humbly in our God confiding,
   Conscious of His love abiding,
   Yes, we feel and understand
   That He dwelleth in our land.

SWITZERLAND

Rufst du, mein Vaterland
J. R. WYSS 1811

Ci chiami, o patria
PIETRO PERI

O monts indépendants
H. RÖHRICH

Hymnus patriotic
APORTA

Composer unknown
Harm. HENRI KLING (1842-1918)

Solenne

Ger. 1. Rufst du, mein Va - ter - land, sich uns mit
Fr. 1. O monts in - dé - pen - dants, Ré - pé - tez
It. 1. Ci chiami, o Pa - tri - a, U - ni - ti im -
Rom.1. Cla - ma'ns o Pa - tri - a, Me - ra'ns u -
Eng. 1. Fa - ther - land, at your call, We of - fer

Herz und Hand all' dir ge - weiht. Heil dir, Hel -
nos ac-cents, Nos li - bres chants! A toi, pa -
- pa - vi - di Snu - diam l'ac - ciar! Sa - lu - te El -
- nits a - quà, Pronts at ser - vir. Il pü cus -
you our all, Our heart, our life. Hail to Hel -

- ve - ti - a! Hast noch der Söh - ne ja, wie sie_ Sankt
- tri - e, Suis - se ché - ri - e, Le sang, la_
- ve - zi - a! Tuoi pro - di fi - gli, Mo - rat, Sant
- tai - vel bain Gu - gent nus't de - di - chain, Per tai_ nus_
- ve - tia's name; Your sons are still the same As those who

This is a popular national song, used on many occasions.
Its tune is the same as that used for Great Britain.
By permission of Foetisch Frères S.A., Lausanne, from *Unsere Schweizerlieder*

Ja - kob sah, freud - voll zum Streit! Streit!
vi - e De__ tes en - fants. fants.
Ja - co - po, Non ob - li - ar! - ar!
vi - ver v'lain, Schi eir mu - rir. - rir.
built your fame, Joy - ful in strife. strife.

GERMAN

2. *Da, wo der Alpenkreis*
   Dich nicht zu schützen weiss,
   Wall dir von Gott.
   Stehn wir den Felsen gleich,
   Nie vor Gefahren bleich,
   Froh noch im Todesstreich,
   Schmerz uns ein Spott.

3. *Frei und auf ewig frei,*
   Sei unser Feldgeschrei,
   Hall unser Herz!
   Frei lebt, wer sterben kann,
   Frei, wer die Heldenbahn
   Steigt als ein Tell hinan,
   Nie hinterwärts!

FRENCH

2. *Nous voulons nous unir,*
   Nous voulons tous mourir
   Pour te servir.
   O notre mère!
   De nous sois fière,
   Sous ta bannière
   Tous vont partir.

3. *Gardons avec fierté*
   L'arbre au Grütli planté,
   La Liberté!
   Que d'âge en âge,
   Malgré l'orage,
   Cet héritage
   Soit respecté.

ITALIAN

2. *La dove è debole*
   Dell'Alpi l'egida
   Che il ciel tidiè
   Ti farem argine
   Coi petti intrepidi
   Anzi che cedere
   Morrem perte.

3. *Ma quando arrideci*
   Di pace l'iride,
   Grazie al Signor
   Ti vogliam florida,
   Diletta patria,
   Col saggio assiduo
   Nostro lavor.

ROMANSCH

2.   *Scha per cas ün regent*
   Ans voless far spavent
   Oun spad e fö,
   Schi sco ün ferm torrent
   Chi sdrapa tuot davent,
   Sün l'inimi crudain
   E'l fain dar lö.

3.   *Flurescha Patria,*
   In pasch e libertà
   Ed uniun!
   Sajan sincerità,
   Güsti 'ed onestà,
   Virtüd, simplicità
   Teis ornamaints.

English Translation (unofficial) by J.J.F.S.

2.   Where the great Alpine shield
   Can no protection yield,
   God will sustain.
   Rocklike, we shall not fail,
   In danger never pale,
   Meet death without a wail
   And smile in pain.

3.   Free and for ever free!
   This shall our watchword be,
   Our heartfelt prayer.
   Free are they who can die,
   And who with purpose high
   To every task apply
   A courage rare.

SYRIA

Words by
KHALIL MARDAM BEY

Music by
AHMAD and MUHAMMAD FLAYFEL
Arr. by **HENRY COLEMAN**

Adopted c. 1928

Ru - bu -'u al-sha-a - mi bur-u - ju al'al - ai Tu - ha - ki sa - ma - a

bi - 'a - li al sa — nai Fa - ar - dhun za - hat

bil - shum-usa al-wid - hai Sa - ma - un la'am-ri - ka aw kal-sa-ma.

TRANSLATION

Defenders of the realm	Syria's plains are
Peace on you;	Towers in the heights,
Our proud spirits will	Resembling the sky
Not be subdued.	Above the clouds.
The abode of Arabism,	A land resplendent
A hallowed sanctuary;	With brilliant suns,
The seat of the stars,	Becoming another sky
An inviolable preserve.	Or almost a sky.

TANGANYIKA
Mungu Ibariki Afrika

Words by a group of
Tanganyikans

Music by ENOCH SONTONGA*
Arr. by V. E. WEBSTER

* By permission of Lovedale Press, Cape Province, South Africa
The words of this anthem are composed from the six prize-winning
entries to the competition announced by the Minister of Education
on 31st July 1961. It became the National Anthem when Tanganyika
achieved independence on 9th December 1961
The music is a shorter version of N'kosi Sikelel'i Africa

Official English Translation

1. God Bless Africa.
   Bless its leaders.
   Let Wisdom Unity and
   Peace be the shield of
   Africa and its people.

   CHORUS Bless Africa
   Bless Africa
   Bless the children of Africa.

2. God Bless Tanganyika.
   Grant eternal Freedom and Unity
   to its sons and daughters.
   God Bless Tanganyika and its People.

   CHORUS Bless Tanganyika
   Bless Tanganyika
   Bless the children of Tanganyika.

THAILAND
Sanrasoen Phra Barami

Words by
H.R.H. Prince NARISARANUVADTIVONGS,
modified c. 1913 by
King RAMA VI (King VAJIRAVUDH)
Unofficial free translation

Music by
—. HUVITZEN

Andante maestoso

Kha wo-ra put-ta chao___ Ao ma-no lae si-ra
Hail to___ our King!___ Bless-ings on___ our

krarn ___ Nop-pra pu-mi barn bu-na-ya-di-rek___
King! ___ Hearts_ and_ heads we___ bow___

Ek bo-ro-ma cha-ka rin Pra sa-ya-min pra yot-sa ying
To Your Ma-jes-ty___ now, Of_ our_ loy-al-ty we

By permission of Department of Fine Arts of the Thai Government.
Adopted as National Anthem, 1934
The music was composed in 1872 for King Rama V (King Chulalongkorn)

TOGO

Words by ALEX CASIMIR-DOSSEH
Trans. from French to Ewe by the
REV. FATHER H. KWAKUME

Music by
ALEX CASIMIR-DOSSEH
Arr. by HENRY COLEMAN

This National Anthem was chosen as a result of a competition
between Togolese composers. It was first played on 27th April,
1960, the date on which Togo attained independence.

f più mosso

-blo - de koe ne - di. To - go, tsi - tre! Na -
vers la li - ber - té To - go, de - bout! Lut -

- wo ka - lê nu-tsu-toe! Wo a - wa nâ-du dzi a - lo na-ku bon! Ma - wu
- tons sans dé-fail-lan-ce Vain-quons ou mou-rons, mais dans la di - gni - té. Grand Dieu,

Gâ, Wo koe do mi de dzi. Ne To - go la na - no
Toi seul nous as ex - al-tés Du To - go pour la pros -

ff

ngo yim la, To - go - vi, va! Mia-tu De - nyi - gba la!
- pé - ri - té, To - go-lais, viens! Ba - tis-sons la Ci - té.

z

Ewe Words

2. *Miawo do ne le deкawowo me.*
Esia enye miafe dzime dzodzro vevieto
Naneke magbahe mo na miafe nyatiatiaa o.
Miawo'si me ko ye wo dzogbenyui kple wo ngoyiyi le.
Yata miade kluvi-kokutiawo da
Anukwaredidi nano mia me daa!
Mina miasubo Denyigba la!
Togonyigba la nezu nami
Abe hehea fe Sikakpe ene.

French Words

2. *Dans l'unité nous voulons te servir*
C'est bien lá de nos coeurs le plus ardent désir
Clamons fort notre devise
Que rien ne peut ternir.
Seuls artisans de ton bonheur ainsi que de ton avenir,
Brisons partout les chaînes, la traîtrise
Et nons te jurons toujours fidélité
Et aimer, servir, se dépasser,
Faire encore de toi sans nous lasser
Togo Chéri, l'Or de l'Humanité.

English Translation

1. Hail to thee, land of our forefathers,
Thou who made them strong, peaceful and happy,
Men who for posterity cultivated virtue and bravery.
Even if tyrants shall come, thy heart yearns towards freedom.
Togo arise! Let us struggle without faltering.
Victory or death, but with dignity.
God almighty, Thou alone hast made Togo prosper.
People of Togo arise! Let us build the nation.

2. To serve thee in unity is the most burning desire of our hearts.
Let us shout aloud our motto
That nothing can tarnish.
We the only builders of thy happiness and of thy future,
Everywhere let us break chains and treachery,
And we swear to thee for ever faith, love, service, untiring zeal,
To make thee yet, beloved Togo, a golden example for humanity.

TONGA

Harmonised by
HENRY COLEMAN

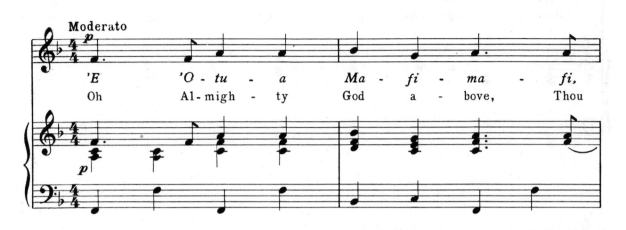

'E 'O - tu - a Ma - fi - ma - fi,
Oh Al - migh - ty God a - bove, Thou

Ko ho mau 'Ei - mi ko - e, Ko Koe ko e
art our Lord and sure de - fence, In our good - ness

fa - la - la 'anga, Mo e 'of - a ki Tong - a:
we do trust Thee And our Ton - ga Thou dost love;

'A - fio hi - fo 'e mau lo - tu
Hear our prayer, for though un - seen We

'Ai - a 'ok - u mau fai ni, Mo ke ta - li
know that Thou hast blessed our land; Grant our earn - est

ho mau lo - to 'O ma-lu - 'i 'a Tu - pou.
sup - pi-ca-tion, Guard and save Tu - pou our Queen.

TRINIDAD AND TOBAGO

Words and Music by
PATRICK S. CASTAGNE (b. 1916)

The National Anthem officially came into use at midnight on
31st August 1962 at the Flag Raising Ceremony held outside
Parliament Buildings at Port of Spain, Trinidad.   It was
chosen as the result of a competition held by the Government.
Patrick Castagne is well known in the West Indies as composer, producer and broadcaster.
Published by permission of the Trinidad and Tobago High Commission, London

TUNISIA

Words by
JALLAL EDDINE ENNAKACHE
English translation by
Dr. ISMAIL HASSAN
Versification by
T. M. CARTLEDGE

Music by
SALAH EL MAHDI
(Piano transcription by
T. M. CARTLEDGE)

HÄ-DUN TA-ḤAL-LÄ BI NAS-RIM-MU-BÎN 'AL-ÄL GhA-SI-BÎN 'AL-
fight is made sweet by a vic-to-ry sure Re-mov-ing the yoke we've

-ÄL HA-KI-MIN TU-GhÂT IZ-ZÄ-MÄN NÄ-
had to en-dure. The fire we con-front as

-KhU-DUL-LÄ HÎB BI RU-HIL HA-BIB ZA-'IM IL-WA-ṬAN
faith-ful we keep The spi-rit of our great lead-er Ha-bib.

Fine

VERSE

1. A - RAL ḤUK-MÄ LISh ShA -'BI FÄN-BÚ LA-NA MI-
1. The peo - ple are sov - 'reign and so let us raise Of

-NÄL MÄDJ -DI A - 'LÄ SU - RÛ - ḤAN TU-ShÄD Ä-
glo - ry a cit - a - del for all to see. O

-DJÍ - BÚ Ä-DJÍ - BÚ LI' - AW-TA-NI-NÄ NI-
ans - wer, O ans - wer our fath - er - land's call To

-DÄ' - ÄL U - KhUW - WÄ - TI WÄL - IT - TI - ḤAD WÄ
true broth - er - hood and to true u - ni - ty. Be

ThÛ - DUL -'I - DÂ 'AN - HI - MÂ AR - DI - NÄ WÄ
rea - dy, like li - ons pre - pared for the fight, De -

KÛ - NÛ U - SÛ - DÄN BI - YÄW - MIL DƷI - LÄD Ä
-fend - ing our coun - try from each en - e - my. Im -

CHORUS

2. WÄRIThNÄL-JILÂDÄ WÄ MÄJDÄN-NIDÂL
WÄ FÎ ARDINÂ MAṢRA 'UL-GhÂṢIBÎN.
WÄ ṢÄLÄT ASÄṬÎLINÂ FIN-NIZÂL
TÄMÛJU BI 'ABṬÄLINÄL-FÂTIḤÎN.
LIWÂ 'UL-KIFÂḤI BIHÂThÄSh-ShIMÂL
RÄFÄ-'NÂHU YÄWMÄL-FIDÂ BIL-YÄMÎN.

3. ShÄBÂBÄL-'OLÂ 'IZZUNÂ BIL-ḤIMÂ
WÄ 'IZZUL-ḤIMÂ BISh-ShÄBÂBIL-'ÄTÎD.
LINÂ HIMMÄTUN ṬÄLÄTIL-'ÄNJUMÂ
TU 'ÎDUL-MÄ 'ÂLÎ WÄ TÄBNIL-JÄDÎD.
FÄḤÄYYUL-LIWÂ KhÂFIQÄN FIS-SÄMÂ
BI 'IZZIN WÄ FÄKhRIN WÄ NAṢRIN MÄJÎD.

2. The glory and fight we inherit today.
Oppressors were fought here on this battleground.
Our legions in fury attacked in the field
As heroes in waves let their war-cries resound.
The banner of war in the North we have raised,
By oath we to ransom our land all are bound.

3. O noble the youth, our defence you assure,
Defending our honour, as ready you be.
Our strong aspirations reach up to the sky
That greatness return and a new day we see.
The flag, as it waves in the sky, now salute
With honour and glory and great victory.

Key to phonetic transliteration of Arabic text

^ for long vowels

Û as *oo* in *pool*

U nearer *u* in *put*

Ä as *a* in *cat*

A as *a* in *rather*

W at end of syllable as *oo*

Th① as *th* in *thing*

Th② as *th* in *this*

Ḥ aspirated at back of mouth

Kh like hard *ch* in German *Buch*

Gh like gutteral *r* in French *rang*

' like last *a* in *China*

Q like *k* sound at back of mouth

TURKEY
Istıklâl Marsi
THE MARCH OF INDEPENDENCE

Words by
MEHMET AKIF ERSOY
English versification by
T. M. CARTLEDGE

Music by
ZEKI ÜNGÖR
Arr. by
T. M. CARTLEDGE

1. *Kork* - *ma* *sön* - *mez* *bu* *şa* - *fak* - *lar* - *da* *yü* - *zen* *al* *san* - *cak* *Sön* - *me* - *den yur* - *du* - *mun üs* - *tün* - *de* *tü* - *ten* *en* *son* *o* - *cak.* O
1. Fear not and be not dis- mayed, This crim - son flag will nev - er fade. It is the last hearth that's burn - ing for my na - tion and we know for

* lower notes optional for bass or alto voices.

Pronunciation: ş like sh
c like j
ö and ü as in German.
ı (i without dot) more like final a of china

Officially adapted as Turkey's National Anthem **12th March 1921**

be - nim mil - le - ti - min._____ Yıl - dı - zı -
sure that it will nev - er fail._____ It is my

-dır par - la - ya-cak. O be - nim - dir,____ o be - nim
na - tion's star that ev - er forth will shine,____ It is my

rall. 2nd volta **ff**

1

2

mil - le - ti - min-dir an - cak.____ 2. Çat -
na - tion's star and it is mine.____ 2. Frown -lâl.____

2. *Çatma kurban olayım çehreni ey nazlı hilâl*
    Kahraman ırkıma bir gül ne bu şiddet bu celâl
    Sana olmaz dökülen kanlarımız sonra helâl
    Hakkıdır hakka tapan milletimin istiklâl.

2. Frown not, fair crescent, for I
    Am ready e'en to die for thee.
    Smile now upon my heroic nation, leave this anger,
        lest the blood shed for thee umblessed be.
    Freedom's the right of this my nation,
    Yes, freedom for us who worship God and seek what's right.

UGANDA

Words by
GEORGE W. KAKOMA and PETER WYNGARD

Music by
GEORGE W. KAKOMA

2. Oh Uganda! the land of freedom.
Our love and labour we give,
And with neighbours all
At our country's call
In peace and friendship we'll live.

3. Oh Uganda! the land that feeds us
By sun and fertile soil grown.
For our own dear land,
We'll always stand:
The Pearl of Africa's Crown.

This National Anthem was selected through a competition, and came
into use when Uganda became independent on 9th October, 1962.
G.W. Kakoma is a Music Master employed in the Education Department,
and P. Wyngard an English Master at Makerere University College.

UKRAINE

Words by
PAUL CHUBYNSKYI (1839-1884)

Music by
MICHAEL VERBYTSKYI (1815-1870)
Arr. by HENRY COLEMAN

Shche ne vmer - la U - kra - i - na, ni sla - va, ni vo - la,

Shche nam brat - tia mo - lo - di - i u - smikh - net' - sia do - la:

Performed as a choral work in 1864 in the Ukrainian Theatre in Lviv,
it became officially recognised as the National Anthem in 1917, but is
not at present used in that country where the U.S.S.R. anthem is officially
used.

Zkhy - nut' na - shi vo - ro-zhen'-ky, yak ro - ssa na son - ci,

Za - pa-nu - yem i my, brat-tia, u svo-ii sto - ron - ci,

Du - shu, ti - lo my po-lo - zhym za na-shu svo-bo - du

I po-ka - zhem, shcho my, brat - tia, ko - zaċ-ko - ho ro - du.

Du - shu ti - lo my po - lo - zhym za na-shu svo-bo - du

I po-ka zhem, shcho my, brat - tia, ko - zać - ko - ho ro - du.

English Translation

Ukraine has not died yet,
As freedom cannot die,
Be hopeful valiant brothers,
Our glory will revive.

Who us enslave, will perish,
As dew within sun's ray,
The enlightened rule of kin
Our country will regain.

Our soul and body willing
To give for liberty,
O, brothers, we are nearing
The path to victory.

UNION OF SOVIET SOCIALIST REPUBLICS

Words by
S. MIKHALKOV and EL-REGISTAN
Translated by
HERBERT MARSHALL

Music by
A.V. ALEXANDROV (d.1946)
Arr. by HENRY COLEMAN

This became officially the Soviet National Anthem
In 1943, replacing the "International".

1. *Soyus neroushimyi respoublik svobodnyh*
   Splotila naveki Velikaya Rousj,
   Da zdravstvouet sozdanny volei narodov
   Ediny, mogouchii Sovetskii Soyus!

   Slavjsya, Otechestvo nashe svobodnoye,
   Drouzhby narodov nadyozhny oplot!
   Znamya sovetskoye, znamya narodnoye
   Poustj ot pobedy k pobede vedyot!

2. *Skvosj grozy siyalo nam solntse svobody,*
   I Lenin velikii nam putj ozaril,
   Nas vyrastil Stalin na vernostj narodu,
   Na troud i na podvigi nas vdohnovil.

3. *Mi armiyu nashu rastili v srazheniah,*
   Zahvatchikov podlyh s dorogi smetyom!
   Mi v bitvah reshayem soudjbu pokolenii,
   Mi k slave Otchiznu svoyu povedyom!

1. Unbreakable Union of freeborn Republics,
   Great Russia has welded forever to stand;
   Created in struggle by will of the peoples,
   United and mighty, our Soviet Land!

   ### CHORUS
   Sing to our Motherland, glory undying,
   Bulwark of peoples in brotherhood strong!
   Flag of the Soviets, peoples' flag flying,
   Lead us from vict'ry to victory on!

2. Through tempests the sunrays of freedom have cheered us,
   Along the new path where great Lenin did lead.
   Be true to the people, thus Stalin has reared us,
   Inspired us to labour and valorous deed!

3. Our army grew up in the heat of grim battle,
   Barbarian invaders we'll swiftly strike down.
   In combat the fate of the future we settle,
   Our country we'll lead to eternal renown.

UNITED ARAB REPUBLIC

Words by
SALAH SHAHYN

Music by
KAMAL ATTAWYL

Wal - la Za-man Ya Si-la — hi Ish-taq-ti Lak Fi Ki-

-fa — hi In - taq We Qul A - na Sa — hi

Ya Har - b Wal - la Za - man.

This was a song which achieved great national popularity in 1956.
The National Anthem was derived from it, and first used on 20th May, 1960.
The chorus only is sung, followed by an instrumental interlude, then a repeat of the chorus.

Transliteration

1. *Walla Zaman 'Algunud*
   Zahfa Bitir'id Ri'ud
   Halfa Tiruh Lam Ti'ud
   Illa Binasr Al-zaman.

2. *Hummu Wu Dummu Al-sufuf*
   Shilu Al-hayat 'Alkufuf
   Yama Al-'adu Rah Yishuf
   Minkum Binar El-fida.

3. *Ya Magd Ya Magdina*
   Yalli Itbanait 'Andana
   Bishaqana Wa Kaddina
   'Umrak Ma Tibqa Hawan.

4. *Masr Al-hurra Min Yihmiha*
   Nihmiha Bislahna
   Ardh Al-thawra Min Yifdiha
   Nifdiha Biarwahna.

5. *Al-sha'b Biyizhaf Zayy El-nur*
   Al sha'b Gebal Al-sha'b Bhur
   Burkan Ghadban Burkan Biyfur
   Zilzal Biyshuqq Lohom Fi Qbur.

Free Translation

Chorus   O! my weapon!
          How I long to clutch thee!
          Respond, awake and alert,
          For valiant combat.

1. Hail, gallant troops,
   Dashing with thunderous roar,
   Swearing never to return
   Except with epoch-making victory.

2. Rise and raise a host,
   With loyal hearts ready for sacrifice.
   Oh! the horror the enemy shall suffer
   Through the fire of your zeal.

3. O! glory of our Country,
   Achieved with our own efforts alone,
   By hard hours of toil,
   Never to be wasted or endangered.

4. Who shall protect Free Egypt?
   We shall protect it with our lives.
   Land of the Revolution, who will sacrifice
   We will, with our lives.   ⌊for her sake?

5. The people advance like the light,
   The people stand like mountains and seas,
   Angry volcanos, erupting volcanos,
   Earthquakes digging graves for the enemy.

UNITED STATES OF AMERICA
The Star-Spangled Banner

Words by
FRANCIS SCOTT KEY (1779-1843)

Music by
J. STAFFORD SMITH
(1750-1836)

Con spirito

1. O ___ say! can you see, by the dawn's ear - ly
stripes and bright stars, thro' the pe - ril - ous

light, What so proud - ly we hail'd at the
fight, O'er the ram - parts we watch'd were so

twi - light's last gleam - ing, Whose broad
gal - lant - ly stream - ing? And the

Words and Music officially designated as the National Anthem
by Act of Congress approved by the President 3rd March 1931.
By permission of J.B. Cramer & Co. Ltd.

rock - ets' red glare, the bombs burst - ing in air, Gave proof thro' the night that our flag was still there. O, say, does that Star - Span - gled Ban - ner yet wave O'er the

CHORUS
Poco meno mosso

land ___ of the free and the home of the brave?

2. On the shore, dimly seen thro' the mists of the deep,
   Where the foe's haughty host in dread silence reposes,
   What is that which the breeze, o'er the towering steep,
   As it fitfully blows, half conceals, half discloses?
   Now it catches the gleam of the morning's first beam,
   In full glory reflected now shines on the stream;
   'Tis the Star-Spangled Banner, O long may it wave
   O'er the land of the free and the home of the brave.

3. O thus be it ever when free man shall stand
   Between their loved homes and the war's desolation!
   Blest with vict'ry and peace, may the heav'n-rescued land
   Praise the Pow'r that hath made and preserved us a nation.
   Then conquer we must, for our cause it is just,
   And this be our motto: "In God is our trust."
   And the Star-Spangled Banner in triumph shall wave
   O'er the land of the free and the home of the brave.

UPPER VOLTA

Words and Music by
Abbé **ROBERT OUÉDRAOGO**
Arr. by **HENRY COLEMAN**

1 Fiè - re Vol - ta de mes A - ïeux, Ton so - leil ar - dent et glo - ri - eux

Te re - vêt d'or et de clar - té, O, Rei - ne dra - pée de lo - yau - té.

CHORUS

Nous te fe - rons et plus forte et plus bel - le,

Approved as the National Anthem by the Upper Volta National Assembly on 3rd August 1960

A ton a-mour, nous res-te-rons fi-dè-les, Et nos cœurs, vi-

-brants de fier-té, Ac-cla-me-ront ta beau-té. -té.

2. Vers l'horizon lève les yeux,
Frémis aux accents tumultueux
De tes fiers enfants tous dressés,
Promesse d'avenirs caressés.

3. Le travail de ton sol brûlant
Sans fin trempera les cœurs ardents,
Et les vertus de tes enfants
Le ceindront d'un diadème triomphant.

4. Que Dieu te garde en sa bonté,
Que du bonheur de ton sol aimé,
L'Amour des frères soit la clé,
Honneur, Unité et Liberté.

Free Translation by ELIZABETH P. COLEMAN

CHORUS We will make thee stronger and more beautiful,
We will stay faithful to thy love,
And our hearts, beating with pride,
Will acclaim thy beauty.

1. Proud Volta of my forefathers,
Thy glorious burning sun
Clothes thee in golden light,
O Queen draped in loyalty.

3. The toil on thy burning soil
Will never cease to brace the fervent hearts
And the virtues of thy children
Will circle it with a triumphal crown.

2. Raise thine eyes towards the future
Vibrating with tumultuous voices
Of thy proud children, standing ready,
The promise of a happy future.

4. May God protect thee in His goodness;
For the happiness of thy beloved land,
May brotherly love be the key
And honour, unity and liberty.

URUGUAY

Words by
FRANCISCO ACŪNA de FIGUEROA (1790-1862)
English versification by
T. M. CARTLEDGE

Music by
FERNANDO QUIJANO and FRANCISCO J. DEBALLI
Arr. by G. GRASSO

Reproduced by permission of
Recordi Americana S.A.E.C. Buenos Aires
Officially adopted as the National Anthem by a government decree of 27th July 1848
The author was a poet and head of the National Library of Uruguay.

sa - bre - mos cum - plir,
ful - fil, cour-age high,

sa - bre - mos cum -
ful - fil, cour-age

- plir, sa - bre - mos cum - plir.
high, ful - fil, cour-age high.

Fine

Moderato

p VERSE

¡Li - ber - tad,! ¡li - ber-tad,! O - rien - ta - les Es - te
Li - ber - ty, Li - ber-ty, East-ern lands - men! 'Twas this

p

grí - to a la Pa - tria sal - vó! Que a sus bra - vos en fie - ras ba -
cry saved our coun-try of yore, And in - flam-ing its he - roes with

mf *p*

-ta-llas, De_en-tu-sias-mo su-bli-me_in-fla-mó. ¡Li-ber-
pas-sion, Pre-pared them for fierce bat-tles' roar. Li-ber-

-mó. De_es-te don sa-cro-san-to la glo-ria me-re-
roar. The___ glo-ry from this gift so sac-red We all

-ci-mos; Ti-ra-nos tem-blad! ¡Ti-ra-nos tem-
mer-it, A-way___ ty-ran-ny! A-way ty-ran-

-blad! Ti-ra-nos tem-blad! Ah! ¡Li-ber-
-ny! A-way, ty-ran-ny! Ah! Li-ber-

- rien - do tam-bien li - ber - tad!
- pir - ing, still cry Li - ber - ty!

ff

tam - bién li - ber - tad!
still cry Li - ber - ty!

tam - bién li - ber - tad!
still cry Li - ber - ty!

dal $\mathsection$ al Fine

f

O - rien -
East - ern

f

dal $\mathsection$ al Fine

VATICAN
Marcia Pontificale

No words

Music by
CHARLES GOUNOD (1818-1893)

This became the official hymn in 1949. It is played (1) In the presence of the Holy Father. (2) In the presence of one of his Special Legates. (3) On the occasion of the presentation of Credential Letters by a Nuncio of the Holy See.

The music is reproduced by permission of Institut fur Auslandsbezihungen, Stuttgart, and taken from *Die National-Hymnen Der Erde*.

VENEZUELA

Words by
VICENTE SALIAS
English versification
by T. M. CARTLEDGE

Music by
JUAN JOSÉ LANDAETA (c. 1810)
Arr. by HENRY COLEMAN

The author and composer, natives of Venezuela, were both shot in
1814 during the struggle for the liberty of their country.
Adopted as National Anthem, 25th May 1881, by a government decree

po - bre en su cho - za li - ber - tad pi - dó: A es - te san - to
poor man in his hov - el Li - ber - ty im - plored. At this ho - ly

nom - bre tem-bló de pa - vor, el vil e - go - is - mo
name There trembled sore with fear The foul self - ish ty - rant,

que otra vez triun - fó. A es - te san - to nom - bre tem-bló de pa -
Who once triumphed here; At this ho - ly name There trembled sore with

- vor, el vil e - go - is - mo que otra vez triun - fó.
fear The foul self - ish ty - rant, Who once triumphed here,

el vil e - go - is - mo que otra vez triun - fó.
The foul self - ish ty - rant Who once tri - umphed here.

2   *Gritemos con brío:*
Muera la opresión!
Compatriotas fieles
la fuerza es la unión:
y desde el Empireo
el Supremo Autor
un sublime aliento
al pueblo infundió.

     CORO

3   *Unida con lazos*
que el cielo formó,
la América toda
existe en Nación;
y si el despotismo
levanta la voz
seguid el ejemplo
que Caracas dió.

     CORO

2 Let's cry out aloud:
May oppression banished be!
Faithful countrymen, your strength
Lives in your unity.
And from highest heaven
The great Creater breathed;
A spirit sublime
Among us here bequeathed.

    CHORUS

3 United by bonds
Made by heav'n's creative hand,
All America exists
As one united land.
And if tyranny
Should dare to raise its head,
Let all of us follow
Where Caracas has led.

    CHORUS

VIET-NAM

Quôc Thiêù Viêt-Nam

Words and Music by
LUU HUU PHUOC, 1943

Này Thanh-niên ơi đứng lên đáp lời sông núi ____ Đồng lòng cùng

đi đi đi mờ đường khai lối. ____ Vì non sông nước xưa, truyền

muôn năm chớ quên. Nào anh em Bắc-Nam cùng nhau tả kết đoàn. Hồn

Adopted as National Anthem in 1945

thanh xuân nhủ gương trong sáng._____ Dừng tiếc máu nóng tài xin

ráng._____ Thời khó thế khó khó làm yêu ta, Dẫu muôn chông gai vững

lòng chi sá Đường mối kiếp phóng mắt nhìn xa bốn phường Tung

cánh hồn thiếu niên ai đó can - trường. Thanh-niên ơi!_____ ta quyết đi

đêń · cùng. Thanh-niên oi!____ ta ngùyên đem hêt lòng Tiêń lên! đông tiêń ve

vang đời sôńg. Chờ quên răńg ta là giôńg Lạc - Hôǹg. ____

Free Translation

Youth of Viet-nam, arise! And at our Country's call
Single in heart let us open the way; let us keep in mind
Our millenary history. From North to South, brothers,
Let us unite. Our young hearts are crystal pure;
Unsparing of our ardent blood, let our efforts increase.
No danger, no obstacle can hold us back.
Despite a thousand trials our courage is unshaken.
On this new road our eyes embrace the horizon,
Our soaring youthful spirit is undauntable.
Youth of Viet-nam, to the very end! this we resolve.
To give ourselves completely, this we vow.
Forward together for a glorious life,
Remember we are the sons of the Lac - Hong.

WALES
Hen Wlad fy Nhadau
LAND OF MY FATHERS

Welsh words by
EVAN JAMES
(1809-1893)
English Translation by
W. S. GWYNN WILLIAMS

Melody by
JAMES JAMES (1856)
Arr. by **W. S. GWYNN WILLIAMS**

Mae hen wlad fy nhad-au yn an nwyl i__ mi, Gwlad beirdd a chan-tor-ion, en-wog-ion o fri; Ei gwr-ol ry-fel-wyr, gwlad-gar-wyr tra__ mâd, Tros rydd-id coll-as-ant eu gwaed.__ Gwlad, gwlad,

The land of my fath-ers is dear un-to__ me, Old land where the min-strels are hon-oured and free; Its war-ring de-fen-ders so gal-lant and__ brave, For free-dom their life's blood they gave.__ Home, home,

CHORUS

This national song was first sung at the famous Llangollen Eisteddfod of 1858, and is now regarded as having the status of a National Anthem. It is also sung as a National Anthem in Brittany, to a Breton transla-tion by Taldir.

By permission of The Gwyn Publishing Co. (Copyright 1950)

pleid - iol wyf i'm gwlad, Tra môr yn fur i'r
true am I to home, While seas se - cure the

bur hoff bau, O bydd - ed i'r hen-iaith bar - hau.
land so pure, O may the old lan-guage en - dure.

2. *Hen Gymru fynyddig, paradwys y bardd,*
   Pob dyffryn, pob clogwyn i'm golwg sydd hardd;
   Trwy deimlad gwladgarol, mor swynol yw si
   Ei nentydd, afonydd, i mi.

   Gwlad, gwlad, etc.

3. *Os treisiodd y gelyn fy ngwlad tan ei droed,*
   Mae hen iaith y Cymry mor fyw ag erioed;
   Ni luddiwyd yr awen gan erchyll law brad,
   Na thelyn berseiniol fy ngwlad.

   Gwlad, gwlad, etc.

2. Old land of the mountains, the Eden of bards,
   Each gorge and each valley a loveliness guards;
   Through love of my country, charmed voices will be
   Its streams, and its rivers, to me.

   Home, home, etc.

3. Though foemen have trampled my land 'neath their feet,
   The language of Cambria still knows no retreat;
   The muse is not vanquished by traitor's fell hand,
   Nor silenced the harp of my land.

   Home, home, etc.

WESTERN SAMOA
The Banner of Freedom

Words and Music by
SAUNI I. KURESA (b.1904)
Arr. by HENRY COLEMAN

Moderato

Sa - moa, tu - la'i ma si - si ia lau fu'a, lou

pa - le le - a; Sa - moa, tu - la'i ma

si - si ia lau fu'a, lou pa - le - le - a; Va -
ʻu -

fe - fe, o le Atua lo ta fa'a vae— O lo - ta

Sa'o lo - to - ga, Sa - moa, tu - la'i, ia

a - gia - gia lau Fu'a lou pa - le le - a.

Samoa, arise and raise your banner that is your crown.

Oh! see and behold the stars on the waving banner
They are a sign that Samoa is able to lead.

Oh! Samoa hold fast
Your freedom for ever.

Do not be afraid; as you are founded on God;
Our treasured precious liberty.
Samoa, arise and wave
Your banner that is your crown.

YEMEN

Arr. by HENRY COLEMAN

Sa-lim-ta I-ma - man Li 'ar - shil - bi la - di

wa-raf-ra-fa haw - la__'u - la - kal__'a - lam

wa'Ish lil ka-ra - ma - ti fi kul - li nad
ma-li - kan li 'ar - shil hu - da Wal hi - mam.

Free Translation

May you be safe as to the country's throne Imam,
And may the herald round your glory flutter,
For by your will corruption's reign dissolved,
And next to pen the sword to you did bow.
May you live long to be in strife the head,
In peace to be abreast, and of philanthropy the King.
May you live long for dignity in every sphere,
And of the throne of piety and zeal the monarch.

YUGOSLAVIA

Words by
(1) JOVAN DJORDJEVIC (1826-1900)
(2) ANTUN MIHANOVIĆ (1796-1861)
(3) ŚIMÓN JENKO (1835-1869)

Music by
(1) DAVORIN JENKO (1835-1914)
(2) LICHTENEGGER (c. 1850)
(3) DAVORIN JENKO (1835-1914)
Arr. by HENRY COLEMAN

Andante Maestoso

Bo - že__ prav - de,__ ti što__ spa - se, Od pro - pa - sti
God of__ Jus - tice,__ Thou who__ saved us When in__ deep - est

do sad nas, Čuj i__ od sad na - še__ gla - se
bond - age__ cast, Hear thy__ coun - try's child - ren's__ voi - ces,

I od - sad nam bu - di - spas! Le - pa na - ša
Be our__ help as in the__ past. Dear and love - ly

This National Anthem is a combination, made in 1918, of the National Anthems of the Serbs, Croats and Slovenes. Part 1 is taken from the Serbian Anthem, Part 2 from the Croatian, Part 3 from the Slovene, and the last 4 bars from the Serbian.
The National Anthem "Hej Slaveni" is now officially used in Yugoslavia.
First four lines of the English translation are by Elizabeth Christich, and the remaining lines by Martin Shaw, copyright J.B. Cramer & Co. Ltd.

YUGOSLAVIA
Hej Slaveni

Words Anon.

Traditional
Arr. by HENRY COLEMAN

Hej Sla-ve - ni, jo - šte ži - vi__ duh na - ših dje -
Fel - low Slavs, the spi - rit of__ your__ an-cient breed still

-do - va, dok za na - rod sr-ce bi - je__
tri - umphs, while your youth still knows the cause__ of the

nij-ho-vih si - no - va. Ži - vi, ži - vi, duh sla-ven - ski
wor-ker and the pea - sant. Long to live Slav - on - ic spi - rit

Originally composed about the middle of the 19th century as
an anthem of the Slavonic movement for the Union of Slavs
and afterwards adopted by some of the Slavonic countries as
their National Anthem. It became the National Anthem of
Yugoslavia in 1945.

ži - vjet ćeš vje - kov - ma, za - lud prije - ti
through all com - ing a - ges, id - le threats or

rall. last time

po - nor pa - kla za - lud va - tra gro - ma.
hell's de - vi - ces, id - le force or ter - ror.

rall. last time

3 Let the tempest rage about us,
     Sweeping all before it —
     Rock is riven, oak uplifted,
     Aye, the whole earth trembles,—

4 But we stand steadfast and constant
     Like a granite mountain.
     Curses be on all betrayers
     False to our glad homeland!

ZANZIBAR

Music by
DONALD FRANCIS TOVEY
Arr. HENRY COLEMAN

Maestoso alla Marcia

The melody on which the anthem is based was well known in Zanzibar for many years.
In 1911 His Highness Sayyid Khalifa bin Harib arranged to have the melody incorporated
into a National Anthem, and this was done by Professor D.F. Tovey.

BAHRAIN

QATAR

NATIONAL DAYS

AFGHANISTAN	27 May	*Independence Day, 1919*
ALBANIA	11 January	*National Day, 1946*
	29 November	*National Day, 1944*
ANDORRA	8 September	*Jungfrau von Meritxell Day (Patron Saint of Andorra)*
ARGENTINE	25 May	*National Day (Anniversary of May Revolution, 1810)*
	9 July	*Independence Day, 1816*
AUSTRALIA	26 January	*Australia Day, 1788*
	25 April	*Anzac Day, 1915*
AUSTRIA	27 April	*Anniversary of the Foundation of the Second Republic, 1945*
	15 May	*Signing of Austrian State Treaty, 1955*
BELGIUM	21 July	*National Day, 1831*
BOLIVIA	9 April	*Anniversary of the National Revolution, 1952*
	6 August	*Anniversary of Independence, 1825*
BRAZIL	7 September	*Independence Day, 1822*
BULGARIA	9 September	*National Day, 1944*
BURMA	4 January	*Independence Day, 1948*
	12 February	*Union Day, 1947*
	27 March	*Armed Forces Day, 1945*
CAMBODIA	9 November	*Independence Day, 1945*
CAMEROON	1 January	*Independence Day, 1960*
CANADA	1 July	*Canada Day (Anniversary of Confederation, 1867)*
CENTRAL AFRICAN REPUBLIC	13 August	*Independence Day, 1960*
CEYLON	4 February	*Independence Day, 1948*
CHAD	11 August	*Independence Day, 1960*
CHILE	18 September	*Independence Day, 1810*
CHINA (National)	10 October	*Proclamation of Republic of Dr. Sun Yat-Sen, 1911*
CHINA (Communist)	1 October	*Proclamation of Provisional Constitution, 1949*
COLOMBIA	20 July	*Independence Day, 1810*
CONGO (Brazzaville)	15 August	*Independence Day, 1960*
CONGO (Leopoldville)	30 June	*Independence Day, 1960*
COSTA RICA	15 September	*Independence Day, 1821*
CUBA	20 May	*Independence Day, 1902*
CZECHOSLOVAKIA	1 August	*Anniversary of the Liberation, 1945*
DAHOMEY	1 August	*Independence Day, 1960*
DENMARK	11 March	*Birthday of H.M. King Frederik IX, 1899*
	5 June	*Constitution Day, 1849*
DOMINICAN REPUBLIC	27 February	*Independence Day, 1844*
ECUADOR	10 August	*Independence Day, 1809*
EIRE	17 March	*St. Patrick's Day*
EL SALVADOR	15 September	*Independence Day, 1821*
ENGLAND	23 April	*St. George's Day*
ETHIOPIA	5 May	*Anniversary of the Restoration of Independence, 1941*
	23 July	*Birthday of H.I.M. Haile Selassie I, 1891*
FAROE ISLANDS	29 July	*National Day*
FINLAND	6 December	*Independence Day, 1917*
FRANCE	14 July	*Bastille Day, 1789*
GABON	17 August	*Independence Day, 1960*
GERMANY	17 June	*Day of Unity*

GHANA	6 March	*Independence Day, 1957*
GREECE	25 March	*Independence Day, 1821*
GUATEMALA	15 September	*Independence Day, 1821*
GUINEA	2 October	*Proclamation of the Republic, 1958*
HAITI	1 January	*Independence Day, 1804*
HONDURAS	15 March	*Thanksgiving Day*
	15 September	*Independence Day, 1821*
HUNGARY	4 April	*Anniversary of the Liberation, 1945*
ICELAND	17 June	*Anniversary of Establishment of the Republic, 1944*
	1 December	*Independence Day, 1918*
INDIA	26 January	*Republic Day, 1950*
	15 August	*Independence Day, 1947*
INDONESIA	17 August	*Independence Day, 1945*
IRAN	5 August	*Constitution Day*
	26 October	*Birthday of H.I.M. Mohammed Reza Shah Pahlevi, 1919*
IRAQ	14 July	*National Day*
ISRAEL	13 May	*Independence Day, 1948*
ITALY	2 June	*Anniversary of Proclamation of the Republic, 1946*
IVORY COAST	7 August	*Independence Day, 1960*
JAMAICA	1st Monday in August	*Independence Day, 1962*
JAPAN	29 April	*Birthday of H.M. The Emperor, 1901*
	3 May	*Constitution Day*
	3 November	*Cultural Day*
JORDAN	25 May	*Independence Day, 1946*
KOREA	15 August	*Independence Day, 1948*
LAOS	11 May	*National Day (Constitution Day), 1947*
	19 July	*Independence Day, 1946*
LEBANON	22 November	*Independence Day, 1943*
LIBERIA	26 July	*Independence Day, 1847*
LIBYA	24 December	*Independence Day, 1951*
LIECHTENSTEIN	16 August	*Birthday of H.S.H. Prince Franz-Josef II, 1906*
LUXEMBOURG	23 June	*National Day*
MADAGASCAR	26 June	*Proclamation of Independence, 1960*
	14 October	*National Day*
MALAYA	1 February	*Setting up of the Federation, 1948*
	31 August	*Merdeka Day, 1957*
MALI	22 September	*Independence Day, 1960*
MALTA	8 September	*National Day, 1565 and 1940/3*
MAURITANIA	28 November	*Independence Day, 1960*
MEXICO	16 September	*National Day, 1810*
MONACO	19 November	*National Day*
MOROCCO	7 March	*Independence Day, 1956*
NEPAL	18 February	*National Day, 1952*
NETHERLANDS	30 April	*Birthday of H.M. Queen Juliana, 1909*
NEW ZEALAND	6 February	*New Zealand Day, 1840*
	25 April	*Anzac Day, 1915*
NICARAGUA	15 September	*Independence Day, 1821*
NIGER	3 August	*Independence Day, 1960*
	18 December	*National Day*
NIGERIA	1 October	*Independence Day, 1960*
NORWAY	17 May	*Constitution Day, 1814*

PAKISTAN	23 March	*Republic Day, 1956*
	14 August	*Independence Day, 1947*
PANAMA	3 November	*Independence Day, 1903*
PARAGUAY	14 May	*Independence Day, 1811*
	25 November	*Constitution Day, 1870*
PERU	28 July	*Independence Day, 1821*
PHILIPPINES, The	4 July	*Independence Day, 1946*
POLAND	22 July	*Constitution Day, 1952*
PORTUGAL	10 June	*National Day*
RUMANIA	9 May	*National Independence Day, 1877*
	23 August	*Anniversary of the Liberation, 1944*
SAN MARINO	3 September	*National Day*
SAUDI ARABIA	20 May	*Independence Day, 1927*
SENEGAL	4 April	*Independence Day, 1960*
SIERRA LEONE	27 April	*Independence Day, 1960*
SINGAPORE	3 June	*National Day, 1959*
SOMALI	1 July	*Independence Day, 1960*
SOUTH AFRICA, UNION OF	31 May	*Union Day, 1910*
SPAIN	2 May	*Independence Day*
	18 July	*Labour Day (celebrated as Spanish National Day), 1936*
SUDAN	1 January	*Independence Day, 1956*
SWEDEN	6 June	*National Day, 1809*
SWITZERLAND	1 August	*Anniversary of the Foundation of Confederation, 1291*
SYRIA	17 April	*National Day, 1943*
TANGANYIKA	9 December	*Republic Day, 1961*
THAILAND	24 June	*National Day, 1932*
TOGO	27 April	*Independence Day, 1960*
TONGA	11 October	*Anniversary of H.M. Queen Salote's Coronation, 1918*
TRINIDAD AND TOBAGO	31 August	*National Day, 1962*
TUNISIA	1 June	*National Day*
	25 July	*Anniversary of Proclamation of the Republic, 1957*
TURKEY	29 October	*Proclamation of the Republic, 1923*
UGANDA	9 October	*Independence Day, 1962*
U.S.S.R.	7 November	*Anniversary of the October Socialist Revolution, 1917*
UNITED ARAB REPUBLIC	23 July	*Anniversary of the Revolution, 1952*
UNITED STATES OF AMERICA	4 July	*Independence Day, 1776*
	27 November	*Thanksgiving Day, 1621. (This is celebrated the nearest Thursday to 27 November each year)*
UPPER VOLTA	5 August	*Independence Day, 1960*
	11 December	*National Day*
URUGUAY	25 August	*Independence Day, 1825*
VENEZUELA	5 July	*National Day. (Anniversary of the signing of Independence, 1811)*
VIET NAM	26 October	*Proclamation of the Republic, 1955*
WALES	1 March	*St. David's Day*
WESTERN SAMOA	1 January	*Independence Day, 1962*
YEMEN	3 October	*National Day (Varies)*
YUGOSLAVIA	29 November	*National Day, 1943*